THE INTERNATIONAL
WILDLIFE
ENCYCLOPEDIA

VOLUME 13

THE INTERNATIONAL
WILDLIFE
ENCYCLOPEDIA

GENERAL EDITORS

Dr. Maurice Burton

Robert Burton

MARSHALL CAVENDISH CORPORATION / NEW YORK

CONTENTS

© 1969 B.P.C. Publishing Limited
Printed in Great Britain
Library of Congress Catalog Card No 78-98713

Palm squirrel

There are three kinds of squirrels with this name, and sometimes the giant squirrels **Ratufa** of India and Malaya are included among them. The best known are the palm squirrels of southern Asia, including Ceylon, India, Pakistan and the Andaman Islands. The five species of Asian palm squirrels are often called striped palm squirrels because they are striped much like chipmunks (p 436). They have a dense soft fur that is light greyish brown to almost black most of the year, but shows reddish on the head from December to May. There are three light stripes on the back, occasionally there is a further short stripe on each flank. Asian palm squirrels are about 7 in. long head and body with about the same length of bushy tail.

The two species of African palm squirrels are up to 2 ft long, of which about half is a bushy tail. One species lives in the Gabon, Cameroons and Congo. The coat colour is a mixture of red and black, and is yellowish on the underparts, where the hair is often scanty and the skin at times almost naked. The second species, in Ghana and Sierra Leone, is reddish with buff patches and some yellow on the underparts. Again the hair on the underparts is sparse, the skin often naked.

The third kind are sometimes spoken of as the oil-palm or African giant squirrels. There are two species, one in West Africa, Liberia to Ghana, the other farther south, from Kenya to Angola. The first has grizzled fur and a slender black tail, the second is tawny olive to nearly black shading to white or buff underparts and cheeks white to greyish. Its bushy tail is sometimes banded black and white. The length of head and body is 13 in., the tail 16 in.

△ *Rare picture of an equally rare animal, an African palm squirrel* **Epixerus ebii**.

▽ *The stripes on an Indian palm squirrel* **F. palmarum** *are good camouflage in the wild.*

△ *The Indian giant squirrel* **Ratufa indica**.

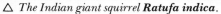
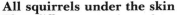

△ *The oil-palm squirrel or 'booming' squirrel as it is sometimes called enjoys a good meal.*

All squirrels under the skin

The different species of striped palm squirrels live in very varied places from open palm forest and scrub at low altitudes to dense jungle with tall trees. Their habits are like those of tree squirrels of the northern hemisphere and like them some palm squirrels live near human settlements even to nesting in roof spaces. African palm squirrels usually live in cavities in trees.

One species *Protoxerus stangeri* is also known as the booming squirrel from the booming sounds it makes when alarmed. Otherwise its voice is a bird-like twittering.

All grist to the mill

Striped palm squirrels feed by day, in the trees or on the ground, on seeds, nuts, stems, bark, buds, leaves and flowers, as well as insects and their grubs. They sometimes take cocoa pods and the buds and seeds of silk cotton trees from which kapok is obtained. They also enjoy eating nectar from the silky oak—which is not a true oak —and in doing so become dusted with pollen and so may act as pollinators. African palm squirrels feed in trees and on the ground, especially on nuts of the oil palm. They have also been known to gnaw fresh ivory and bones.

Surplus males

In the Indian palm squirrel there are as many females born as males but by the time maturity is reached the males outnumber the females. At breeding time a female is chased by several males who fight among themselves while she waits on a nearby tree making peeping calls at her fighting suitors. The successful male then mates with her. Although mating is prolonged, up to 20 minutes, the male stays with the female for only a day. The female builds a nest on the branches of a tree or in a hollow. It is globular, made of dry grass or other fibrous materials such as bits of cloth, jute sacking, animal hair and feathers. One was seen to card a mass of cottonwool, using her incisors and forepaws. Another, in captivity, pulled out the hairs from her own tail to bind the dry grass of the nest. The main breeding season is March—September, but there may be 3 litters a year with 2−4, usually 3, in a litter. The young are born naked, with pink skin, and measure 4 in. long of which more than half is tail. Their eyes are unopened, their ears folded and they cannot crawl until a few days old, and then only feebly. The ears open at 7 days, the eyes between 15−25 days. Weaning is at 25−30 days and the young have grown a full coat of hair, shorter than in the adult but with the same colour and pattern by 5−8 weeks. They are then half the size of the parent. The young females are sexually mature at 6−8 months of age, but there is no information on the age at which young males become sexually mature and search for females.

Squirrel plays 'possum

The North American opossum (p 1615) is well known for its habit of 'shamming dead', and there are only a few reports of other mammals having done this. One is the Indian palm squirrel. DR Sharma, S Sivaram and K Verma have described what happened when one of them shot at a palm squirrel with an airgun. The squirrel fell onto a lower branch as if it had been hit. It hung upside down from the branch, clinging by its hindfeet, the head hanging limply, the eyes half-closed, and the grip of the hindfeet showing signs of relaxing. All were convinced the squirrel had been fatally injured although no blood was showing. Then one of them climbed up the tree and stretched out a hand to take the squirrel. But it suddenly started moving and quickly ran down the tree, running away faster than any of them could follow.

class	**Mammalia**
order	**Rodentia**
family	**Sciuridae**
genera & species	***Epixerus spp*** *African palm squirrels* ***Funambulus spp*** *Indian palm squirrels* ***Protoxerus stangeri*** *oil-palm squirrel, others*

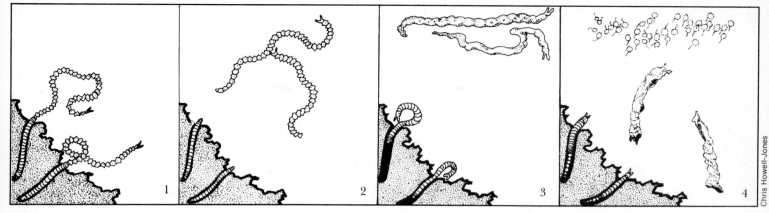

Palolo worm

Twice a year, and with incredible regularity, half of this worm develops almost into another animal, and swarms of these invade the sea to breed. Palolo worms measure about 16 in. long, and, like their relatives the ragworms, are divided into a large number of segments each with a pair of paddle-like appendages that bear gills. The head has several sensory tentacles and an evertable pharynx which has stout teeth. Males are reddish-brown and females bluish-green.

The palolo worm lives in coral reefs off Samoa and Fiji in the southern Pacific, but related worms live in shallow seas in other tropical regions.

Mass wedding

Palolo worms riddle coral with the tubes that they dig in the reefs, in crevices, or under rocks. They are very difficult to extract whole because their long, fragile bodies are firmly anchored in the tubes.

Towards the breeding season the back half of the body of a palolo worm alters drastically. The muscles and other internal organs degenerate while the reproductive organs in each segment grow rapidly. The limbs become more paddle-like. In due course the palolo worm backs up its tunnel, with the head innermost, until the modified portion of its body is protruding. This part breaks free and swims to the surface as a separate animal, complete with rudimentary eyes with which to navigate. The remaining front half stays in the tube and regenerates the lost portion.

These free-swimming portions of the palolo worm were once thought to be the complete animal but they are little more than bags of eggs and sperms. On reaching the surface these are discharged and the empty skins sink to the bottom to be devoured by fish. The eggs are fertilised as they float at the surface and from them free-swimming larvae develop.

This behaviour is a kind of reproduction by proxy, with the worm staying in the safety of its tube while releasing a part of itself to go out and mate. This is incredible enough but the spectacular feature is that all the reproductive parts are released at the same time each year. When this happens the sea becomes a writhing mass of millions of worms and is milky with eggs and sperms.

△ *Spectacular life cycle of Pacific palolo worm. As the breeding season approaches the adults reverse their positions in burrows; the back half alters drastically as the reproductive organs grow rapidly (1). This part breaks free and swims to the surface (2). The remaining adult portions reverse to a normal position. The eggs and sperm sections develop further with internal segments breaking down to give a single sac (3), which soon bursts releasing eggs and sperm so random fertilisation takes place (4). This is neatly timed—millions of worms mating at once.*

Swarming is limited to the neap tides of October and November. It occurs at dawn, the day before and the day on which the moon is in its last quarter.

The advantages

How the palolo worms calculate the time of spawning so accurately is not known; they certainly cannot watch the phases of the moon from their burrows. Presumably they have a very accurate internal 'clock' which is regulated by a combination of a diurnal

Pacific palolo male adult

rhythm of night and day and of tidal changes. In addition to this, there is probably the same stimulus as is mentioned under oyster (p 1656). In oysters, sea urchins and some other marine animals the first sperms released touch off a wholesale spawning. It is possible that the first palolo worms to shed their rear portions into the water for spawning give out a chemical, possibly a hormone, which touches off a similar wholesale action among all the others in the reef that are ready to spawn.

If the mechanism is obscure, the advantages are obvious. By releasing all eggs and sperms in one or two highly synchronised batches the chances of fertilisation are very much increased. In many marine animals, especially those that are sedentary and release eggs and sperms in the sea, there is often a restricted breeding season which increases the chances of the sex cells meeting. Oysters, for instance, 'spat' more frequently at new and full moons than at other times, but few animals attain the narrow limits achieved by the palolo worm. A very closely related species in the West Indies spawns in the third quarter of the June and July moons, while another worm *Ceratocephale osawai* spawns off Japan at the new and full moons of October and November. The grunion (p 972) also has a narrowly regulated mating season.

Seasonal delicacy

For a long time the spawning palolo worms have been caught in vast numbers by the peoples of the South Pacific. Chiefs living by the sea send them inland as presents for they are highly esteemed raw or cooked. In Fiji the time of swarming is heralded first by the flowering of the scarlet aloals and the seasea. Then they know they must watch for the moon being on the horizon as dawn breaks. Ten days after this the palolo worm spawns, The first swarm is 'Mbalolo lailai'—little palolo, and the second 'Mbalolo levu'—large palolo. On the island of Savaii the swarming is forecast, three days beforehand by the mass migration of land crabs down to the sea to spawn themselves.

phylum	**Annelida**
class	**Polychaeta**
family	**Eunicidae**
genus & species	***Eunice viridis*** *Pacific* **E. fucata** *West Indies*

1683

Panda

This black and white bear-like carnivore has leapt from obscurity to worldwide fame in less than a century. Also called the giant panda and, by the Chinese, **beishung**, the white bear, it was first made known to the western world in 1869, by the French missionary, Père David. It has usurped the name from the cat-bear (p 391), which was originally called panda, but is now called the lesser or red panda, or cat-bear, to distinguish the two.

The panda is stockily built, with a 6 ft long body and a mere stump of a tail and weighs 300 lb. Its thick, dense fur is white except for the black legs and ears, black round the eyes and on the shoulders. There are 5 clawed toes on each foot and each forefoot has a small pad which acts as a thumb for grasping. The cheek teeth are broad and the skull is deep with prominent ridges for the attachment of strong muscles needed in chewing fibrous shoots. It lives in the cold damp bamboo forests on the hillsides of eastern Tibet and Szechwan in southwest China.

Zool Soc London

to the Moscow zoo, and Chi-chi, the female in the London zoo. In 1966 Chi-chi was taken to Moscow by air but no mating took place, and An-an was brought to London in 1968 with no more success. It is believed that pandas mate in spring, and that probably one or two cubs are born in the following January, each cub weighing 3 lb at birth. Several cubs have been born in Chinese zoos. On September 9, 1963, a male cub Ming-ming was born to Li-li and Pi-pi in Peking zoo, and a female cub, Ling-ling, was born on September 4, 1964, to the same parents. A third cub Hua-hua, a male, was born to Chiao-chiao on October 10, 1965. According to Mare Ribaud, a French photographer writing in *Natural History,* April 1966, Ming-ming and Ling-ling were produced by artificial insemination. Presumably the same is true for Hua-hua.

▷ *Chinese mother love. Although breeding has not been achieved in the western world, Chinese zoos have bred pandas. The young one seen here cradled in its mother's arms was born at Peking Zoo. Although it was thought that Peking Zoo had a breeding unit of pandas, Mare Ribaud, a French photographer wrote in 1966 that artificial insemination was practised. Breeding behaviour in the wild is still unknown. It is thought that oestrus is in April with a gestation period of 148 days. There are differing views on its numbers in the wild. The director of Peking Zoo in 1966 did not commit himself to any estimate of numbers but thought the number was small. On the other hand he thought the numbers would increase as the local people understood the interest of the animal.*

Conservation co-operation. With the rare species quota increasing each year it is important for today's zoos to try to breed these rarities. Often a zoo has only one sex of an endangered animal, so the director will try to arrange a 'marriage' with the opposite sex if another zoo has the needed partner. 'An-an' (above) of Moscow Zoo and 'Chi-chi' of London Zoo were the only live pandas of the western world in the sixties. The Russians allowed Chi-chi to visit An-an in 1966 (right) but this encounter proved a failure. Chi-chi returned home in disgrace after refusing all An-an's advances. In 1968-69 An-an spent 10 months with Chi-chi in London Zoo but even after sex hormone treatment she still refused to be mated.

Habits unknown . . .

Pandas are solitary animals except in the breeding season. They live mainly on the ground but will climb trees when pursued by dogs. They are active all the year. Little more is known of the habits in the wild of this secretive animal which lives in inaccessible country. When live pandas were first taken to zoos it was thought they lived solely on bamboo shoots. Later it was learned that during the 10—12 hours a day they spend feeding they eat other plants, such as grasses, gentians, irises and crocuses, and also some animal food. This last includes small rodents, small birds and fishes flipped out of water with their paws.

Breeding unknown . . .

Little is known about the panda's breeding habits in spite of attempts to induce a mating between An-an, the male panda belonging

Ian Watson

Via dolorosa

In 1869 Père Armand David of the Lazarist Missionary Society, and an experienced naturalist, came upon the skin of an animal in a Chinese farmhouse in Szechwan which he did not recognize. He sent it to Paris and later sent more skins. Not until 1937, however, was the first live panda seen outside China. Theodore and Kermite Roosevelt had shot one in the 1920's and in 1936 two other Americans, Ruth and William Harkness, with the animal collector Tangier Smith, captured several. They quarrelled, presumably over the spoils, and all the pandas died except one, which Ruth Harkness delivered to the Chicago zoo where it was named Su-lin. Another, given the name Mei-mei, reached the same zoo in 1938. In December the same year a young female, Ming, aged 7 months and two young males, Tang and Sung, reached the London zoo. The two males died before the female reached maturity, and she died in December

1944. In May 1946, the government of the Szechwan Province presented a male, Lienho, to the London zoo and he lived until 1950. By 1967 there were a score of pandas in various zoos, 16 or more in Chinese zoos, An-an in Moscow and Chi-chi in London.

Whether giant pandas are as rare as is sometimes supposed is a matter for speculation. If it is, this could be due in no small measure to the way they have been treated. Although the species is now protected it was formerly hunted by the local Chinese, and the history of western animal collectors does nothing to offset this. The story of Chi-chi gives point to this. In 1957, Heini Demmer, then living in Nairobi, was commissioned by an American zoo to negotiate the exchange of a collection of East African animals for one panda. He reached Peking zoo with his cargo, was given the choice of one of three pandas, chose Chi-chi, the youngest, and took charge of her on May 5 1958. Chi-chi had been captured by a Chinese team of collectors on July 5 1957,

Bamboo shoots are not the sole food of pandas — other plants and some animal food is eaten.

and was reckoned then to be 6 months old. She had been taken to Peking zoo and cared for night and day by a Chinese girl. By the time Demmer had taken charge of Chi-chi the United States had broken off diplomatic relations with the Chinese People's Republic, so she became automatically a banned import. Demmer took her on a tour of European zoos during the summer of 1958, by car, rail and plane, reaching the London zoo, where she was bought, on September 26.

After such treatment perhaps it is not surprising she refuses to be mated!

class	**Mammalia**
order	**Carnivora**
family	**Procyonidae**
genus & species	***Ailuropoda melanoleuca***

Pangolin

*Pangolins have sometimes been called
animated pine cones because the hair on
their backs has been converted into large
overlapping brown scales covering the
head, back, tail and legs. The underside
of the body is, however, soft and hairy.
The pangolin's body is long, with a long
tail. Its snout is pointed, with a small
mouth at the end and with toothless jaws.
Its long tongue can be thrust out for
nearly a foot. The pangolin has small
eyes and hidden ears. Its legs are short
and the five toes on each foot have stout
claws used in digging. In Africa there are
four species of pangolin, or scaly anteater
as it is sometimes called, and three in
southern Asia.*

*The large African pangolin of equatorial
Africa is 5 ft or more long as is the giant
pangolin. Other African species are the
black-bellied or long-tailed pangolin and
the small-scaled tree pangolin, from
West Africa to Uganda, both 3 ft total
length. The largest Asiatic species is the
Indian pangolin, 3½ ft long. The Chinese
pangolin, of Nepal, southern China,
Hainan and Formosa, and the Malayan
pangolin are both under 3 ft.*

Ground dwellers and tree climbers

Most of these strange scaly beasts climb trees,
using their sharp claws and their tail, either
wrapping the tail around a branch and
sometimes hanging by it, or using it as a
support by pressing it against the trunk of a
tree. The giant and Indian pangolins both
live on the ground, however, the latter sometimes climbing trees for safety when chased.
All pangolins are active mainly at night, the
ground-living forms resting in burrows dug
by other animals, the tree dwellers resting
in cavities in the trunks. When on the
ground they walk on the sides of their forefeet, or on their knuckles, with their long
claws turned inwards. They will sometimes
walk on their hindlegs with their body raised
semi-erect, their tail raised above the
ground as a counterpoise.

Hot meals

This attitude, with the tail supporting the
erect or semi-erect body, is also used when
a pangolin is tearing open a termites' nest
with its long front claws and exploring the
galleries of the nests with its long tongue.
The tongue is sticky and is flicked in and
out to carry the termites into the mouth.
Ants are also eaten: adults, pupae, larvae,
and eggs. The tough skin of the head protects the pangolin from attacks by soldier
termites or the stings of ants. The nostrils
and ear openings can be closed and the eyes
are protected by thick lids. Ants crawling
onto the body are shaken off, and those
swallowed are soon ground by the thick
muscular walls of the stomach and by the
small pebbles that the pangolin swallows.
Tree-climbing pangolins eat mainly tree
ants. A pangolin drinks by rapidly darting
its tongue out and in.

Pangolins do not usually survive long in

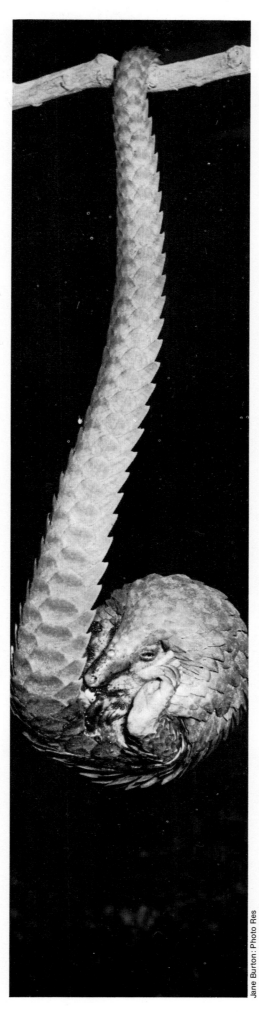

Jane Burton: Photo Res

captivity, a few weeks at most, and post
mortem examinations have shown their
digestive organs to be heavily parasitized.
One lived over 4 years in the New York Zoological Park on finely ground raw beef,
cooked cereal, evaporated milk, ant's eggs,
with occasional raw egg, cod-liver oil and
vitamin concentrate. But it seems likely that
termites and ants are essential to them.

Babies ride pick-a-back

Very little is known about the breeding
habits of pangolins since they fail to breed
in captivity. They have one young, rarely
two, in the wild, probably every year. The
scales do not harden until the second day
after birth. Later the baby rides on the
mother clinging to her tail.

Ant-bathing

The main enemy of pangolins is probably
man. Animals, such as leopards, sometimes
examine them but are, it seems, put off by
their scales. They are killed locally for their
flesh and their scales are used for ornaments
and charms, as well as for their supposed
medicinal value. In Africa boys are sent
into the burrow to put a rope round a
pangolin's tail, to drag it out. Its defence
is to roll up but even a light touch on a
pangolin's body makes it snap its sharp-
edged scales flat and this may act as a
deterrent. Some pangolins, possibly all, can
give off an obnoxious fluid from glands
under their tail. They are said sometimes to
hiss when molested.

There is a story that pangolins allow ants
to crawl under their scales, then snap the
scales down to kill them, afterwards eating
the dead ants. The probable explanation is
that the scales are snapped down because
the observer touches the pangolin, or makes
a movement that alarms it. That they do
take an ant bath seems likely. There are
local beliefs that a pangolin will lie in an
ants' nest, allowing the insects to crawl
over it, and under its scales onto the soft
skin beneath. There are reports about
a variety of animals taking ant baths. It is
presumed they get satisfaction from the
formic acid stimulating the skin. Cecil S
Webb, an animal collector, was of the
opinion that a pangolin's skin absorbed this
acid and it was essential to the animal's
health. He suggested this was one reason
why they failed to survive in captivity.

An animal puzzle

Pangolin skins brought back from Africa
and Asia were known to the Romans and
also to the scientists of the 16th century
and later. All were puzzled by them, as
were the peoples in whose countries they
lived. Arabs called the pangolin *abu-khirfa*,
'father of cattle', the Indians named it *bajur-
kit*, 'jungle fish', the Chinese name was
lungli, 'dragon carp', and the Romans called
it an earth-crocodile. The name 'pangolin'
is from the Malay *peng-goling*, the roller,
from its habit of rolling into a ball. Pangolin
skins puzzled the scholars of Europe until
early 19th century when Baron Cuvier decided it was a mammal.

*It's easy when you have the equipment! A small
scaled pangolin hangs by its prehensile tail.*

Animated pine cones

◁ *A black-bellied pangolin illustrates its common description — 'animated pine cones'.*
▷ *Small-scaled youngster grips to mother's tail while she is curled up asleep.*
▽ *A long elastic tongue protruded from a toothless mouth of a large African pangolin seeks out ants and termites on which it feeds.*

◁ *Ants swarm over the scales of a giant pangolin intent on eating all it can.*
▷ *Pangolins are quite widespread but not very numerous in any part of their range.*
▷▷ *A pangolin rolls itself into a ball.*

class	**Mammalia**
order	**Pholidota**
family	**Manidae**
genus & species	***Manis crassicaudata*** Indian
	M. gigantea large African
	M. javanica Malayan
	M. longicaudata black-bellied
	M. pentadactyla Chinese
	M. temminckii giant
	M. tricuspis small-scaled tree

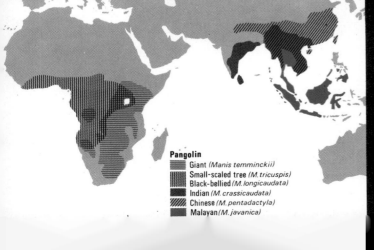

Pangolin

◼ Giant *(Manis temminckii)*
⦀ Small-scaled tree *(M. tricuspis)*
▥ Black-bellied *(M. longicaudata)*
◼ Indian *(M. crassicaudata)*
▨ Chinese *(M. pentadactyla)*
◼ Malayan *(M. javanica)*

Paper wasp

Paper wasps are closely related to the common wasps and hornets of the genus **Vespula** *and* **Vespa**. *There is little to choose between them in appearance, but the thorax and abdomen of the paper wasp are pear-shaped where they join, more like an hourglass than the rounded thorax and abdomen of the other wasps. In habits paper wasps differ by making small nests that are not enclosed by a papery sheath, and the cells containing eggs and larvae are open.*

Paper wasps are found all over the world in tropical and temperate regions. They do not live in Britain but are very common in North America.

often get warm, the nests are kept cool by the wasps fanning their wings, and they may bring water to regurgitate over the comb.

The queen paper wasp constructs the nest from paper which she makes by rasping wood from a tree with her jaws, chewing it and mixing it with saliva. The first stage in building is a flat foundation on the underside of a roof or branch. From this grows a short stalk that holds the main part of the nest—the brood cells which make up the spherical comb.

Family planning

Sometimes in warmer regions several queens combine to build a nest and lay eggs, but eventually one queen asserts her authority and the others stop laying. If, however, the senior queen dies, one of the others will take her place. The ovaries of the lesser queens are small in comparison with those

are left to tend the next generation. The larvae are fed on a paste of caterpillars and other insects that have been chewed up by the adults. The larvae grow fat on this diet and after a few weeks the entrances of their cells are sealed with a thin layer of paper and pupation takes place. After emerging from their cells the new workers take a meal from other workers then start their life's work of raising new generations. The nest gradually increases as new cells are added, but in autumn larvae start to die, probably because of a failing food supply, and the colony dies off. Before this happens the males and queens will have set out on their mating flights. The colonies cannot survive in temperate regions as wasps do not store food as honey bees do. In the tropics and near tropics, however, the workers can hibernate through the brief period of bad weather and then become active again.

◁ *Hibernation between mango tree leaves; female S. African wasps* **Polistes fastidiosus**.

△ *An untimely end. A Jamaican paper wasp is killed by an insect-attacking fungus which grows inside the wasp's body until the wasp dies and the fruiting fungus bursts out.*

JAL Cooke

Cup-shaped nests

The life of the paper wasp is very easy to study because the nest is built above the ground, it is open so that all the activities can be watched and the colony is comparatively small. Some nests may number up to 500 wasps but there are usually less than 100. In small nests it is quite easy to mark all wasps with individual paint marks and to watch and record their behaviour.

In tropical regions the nests survive the year round but in temperate climates the workers and males die in the autumn, leaving the queens to survive the winter by lying dormant in a shelter. In the following spring the queens emerge and seek a suitable place for their nests. As the nests are open the site must not be exposed to strong winds or strong sunlight. A common place for nests is under eaves of houses and sheds, or on branches, but as these places

of the senior queen, but if they do lay eggs she destroys them. The senior queen is also looked after more carefully by the workers than the other queens. How she manages to dominate the nest is not really known but it is probably by means of pheromones, chemicals given off from her body which affect the behaviour and body functions of the other paper wasps.

The queens are fertilised before their winter retreat and the sperms are stored until the eggs are laid. The workers develop from fertilised eggs, but are infertile themselves because they are reared on a reduced diet. Only later in the season are new queens raised by feeding larvae on a rich diet. At the same time males are reared from unfertilised eggs.

The first batch of larvae are reared by the queens but once they have emerged from cocoons as fully fledged worker wasps they

Cuckoo wasps

The life of social insects—bees, wasps and ants—is a hard one and individual workers do not live long. The ways of these insects have been held up as shining examples of industry, but some species let the side down, and exploit the industry of their relatives. A few species of paper wasps and of the genus *Vespula*, are called cuckoo wasps. The details of their habits are not fully known but it appears that the queens emerge from hibernation after those of the normal species. Each one searches for a flourishing nest and lays her own eggs in it. During this time the reigning queen and the lesser queens as well as the queen larvae and pupae are killed. The cuckoo wasp eggs develop into males and females only, never workers, and these are raised by the host workers to maturity, when they fly off to mate.

The paper nest world of the paper wasp

JAL Cooke

phylum	Arthropoda
class	Insecta
order	Hymenoptera
family	Vespidae
genus	*Polistes annularis*
& species	*P. gallicus* others

*The queen paper wasp builds the small globular nest from paper which she makes by rasping wood from a tree and mixing it with saliva. The nest of **P. smithii** a S. African species (right) contains larvae at various stages and pupae in the capped cells. The wasp on the right is chewing a piece of caterpillar to feed to the larvae. (Above) Another paper wasp tends one of its cells (11 × natural size).*

1695

Papuan turtle

Very few specimens of this freshwater turtle have ever been collected and it is the only living species of its family. Its anatomy is interesting because it is a link between the soft-shelled tortoises of the family Trionychidae and the other cryptodire tortoises, those that withdraw their heads vertically. It is also a relict of a family that once lived in Europe, Asia and North America.

The maximum recorded length of a Papuan turtle is 19 in. Its carapace rises to a peak like the roof of a house while the plastron is flat. The front part of the plastron is connected to the rear portion by stout connective tissue but the shell cannot be closed over the head as in mud turtles (p 1529). The shell is bony and hard but lacks the horny plates that cover the shells of all other tortoises and turtles except the soft-shelled tortoises. The head has a long snout with two tubular nostrils and sharp horny cutting edges on the jaws. The limbs are paddle-like, similar to those of sea turtles. The third, fourth and fifth fingers are long but the short first and second fingers have strong claws. The skin is grey-brown and soft and the blood vessels are faintly discernible through it.

Papuan turtles are confined to the lowlands of southern New Guinea and have been found in only a few parts of this region. As so little collecting has been done in New Guinea it is difficult to know whether the Papuan turtle really is rare.

Not active

Nothing is known of the breeding habits of the Papuan turtle but it is thought that the only time it ever comes on land is to lay eggs. The rest of its life is spent in water. Most specimens have been found in the brackish water of estuaries but some have been found farther up rivers and in lakes. The flippers and the light, streamlined body suggest that Papuan turtles are active swimmers living in open water, but they are found in shallow water near the bottom and one of the functions of the strong, broad claws is to anchor the turtle to a rock or log. The claws are also used to hold prey that cannot be swallowed whole. While the food is held firm pieces can be bitten off by the jaws. In captivity Papuan turtles have fed on lettuce and apples, meat, worms, pond snails and young mice. Live fishes were ignored, which supports the idea that Papuan turtles are sluggish and feed only on plants, slow-moving animals and carrion.

Underwater breathing

At intervals a Papuan turtle leaves the bottom and swims steeply to the water surface to breathe, but like other aquatic tortoises and turtles it gets a fair proportion of its oxygen from the water. It may be that it does this partly through its skin since blood vessels can be seen near the surface of the soft skin. Moreover, when lifted from the water a Papuan turtle expels water from its cloaca, so exchange of oxygen and other gases could take place in the hind part of the intestine, as happens in some fishes. It also seems likely that the mouth is a site for gas exchange, just as some fishes and frogs use the lining of the mouth as a sort of lung. While the turtle is resting on the bottom the throat can be seen pumping about 24 times each minute. Water is drawn in through a gap between the jaws and is ejected through the nose and mouth. This water current may also enhance the sense of smell as chemicals will be drawn through the nose. These ideas are partly conjectural and will not be made certain until more Papuan turtles are kept in captivity.

△ *Rare or not? Very few specimens of this freshwater turtle have ever been collected.*

Fixing the reward

Collecting rare animals is often simplified by offering local people a reward for specimens. There are drawbacks, however. The story was recounted on page 799 of how the supposedly rare Madagascan fly was found in swarms on a native cow; and in England a zoologist living in a seaside town in the 1880's offered a reward for each specimen of a small sponge called a sea orange, which he thought was rare. The next day a barrel packed with 1 in. sea oranges arrived at his door. But the search for Papuan turtles took an opposite turn to these embarrassing events. A German collector once managed to bring live Papuan turtles back to Europe. On arriving at a small village in Papua he had offered a reward for live Papuan turtles. In due course a number of turtles were brought in, but none was a Papuan turtle. One day a villager told the collector, quite incidentally, that he had a long-nosed turtle that was especially good to eat. The collector realised his mistake. He was offering too low a price for turtles that were worth more as food, so he increased his reward sufficiently to overcome the villagers' desire for turtle meat and in a few days had collected nine live specimens. The moral of these stories is that animals not well known to scientists may be well known to the local people, but care must be taken when trying to get hold of them.

class	**Reptilia**
order	**Chelonia**
family	**Carettochelidae**
genus & species	***Carettochelys insculpta***

Paradise fish

This is the fish that first made tropical aquarium keeping popular. People have been keeping goldfish for a long time but it was in the mid-19th century that home aquaria became the rage. At first marine animals and a few freshwater fishes were kept in them. Then in 1861, the paradise fish was brought to Paris. Before long it had reached England and other European countries and in 1876 it was taken to the United States. At first aquarists were afraid the new fish would injure their goldfish. But in fact it was the paradise fish that started the fashion of keeping 'tropicals'.

The paradise fish can be up to $3\frac{1}{2}$ in. long and has a body that is flattened from side to side. It has flowing dorsal and anal fins, a large rounded tail, small pectoral fins and pelvic fins about the same size as the pectorals and lying beneath them. The male is brown to greenish-grey with marbling on the head and a large blackish spot ringed with orange on each gill cover. The flanks are banded blue-green and carmine. The fins are reddish, the pelvics white-tipped and the dorsal and anal fins have dark spots. The female is similar but paler.

The range of the paradise fish is from Korea through eastern China, including Formosa, to South Vietnam. A second species, the round-tailed paradise fish, similar but slightly smaller, has much the same range but does not go so far south. A third species, also small, with two longitudinal bands on the flanks, ranges from India and Ceylon, through Burma to South Vietnam.

Wild or tame

Much has been written about the paradise fish in scientific and aquarist journals, discussing two aspects of it: whether it is the wild form or one bred by the Chinese, and what is the purpose of its bubble nest. No firm conclusions have been reached. On the whole it seems that the fish as we know it in the aquarium is much the same as the fish that is wild in the rice fields. The aquarium breeds have been only slightly altered from the wild forms although there are also special breeds. There is, for example, a dark variety, *concolor*, and there is an albino strain, white with pink eyes and pink bands on the flanks which breeds true.

Bubble blowers unlimited

As in many other labyrinth fishes, paradise fishes build nests of bubbles. The male blows out bubbles of air and mucus which rise to the surface and there form a raft. Then follows an elaborate mating. The colours of the male become brighter as the breeding period draws near, the female becomes paler. When the female is about to spawn the male wraps himself round her while she lies in the normal position just under the bubble raft. As the eggs begin to be laid

the pair make a barrel roll, which brings the female upside-down with the male still wrapped round her, so he fertilises the eggs as they leave her body. Then he releases the female and trembles for a few seconds before gathering any slowly sinking eggs in his mouth, rising to the underside of the bubble nest and spitting the eggs onto it. Unlike other bubble nesters whose eggs are heavier than water, those of the paradise fish mostly float upwards when laid. Only a small percentage fail to do this and slowly sink. When the clutch is complete he blows more bubbles to make a second layer under the eggs, sealing them in. This may be repeated time and time again.

There are several opinions about the purpose of the raft. One is that it protects the eggs from the heat of strong sunlight beating down on the rice fields. Another is that it shades them from strong light. A third is that it protects the eggs from bacteria. The fourth suggestion, and the most likely, is that it keeps the eggs together, and also the fry when they hatch, making it easier for the male to guard them. The eggs hatch in 2 days at a temperature of 26°C/80°F.

Paradise fish can respond to sounds of frequencies between 2 637 and 4 699 cycles per second and there is the possibility that they make sounds, perhaps inaudible to us, which stimulate breeding.

Reason in their quarrelsome habits

Little is known about the enemies of paradise fish in the wild. More is known about their pugnacious nature in aquaria, where they will tear the fins of other kinds of fishes if placed in a mixed tank. They feed on any small animals, being very predatory, and they readily attack members of their own kind. In aquaria care must be taken to keep male and female apart until they are ready to breed, and it may happen that, after mating, the female may be savaged by the male if she has too little

△ *Fashion makers – paradise fish made tropical aquaria popular. Species:* **Macropodus dayi**.

space to get away from him. What purpose is served by this internecine strife is hard to say. Perhaps clues can be found from experimental work that has been carried out on paradise fish in the laboratory. It has been found that they eat more food when grouped together but grow faster when placed in tanks on their own. Their aggressiveness may be purely a matter of keeping each fish spaced out, to give them growing space, or it may be a natural means of controlling numbers.

Females take over

Although the building of the bubble nest and care of the young is normally the work of the male, females have been seen to do both. Presumably, should a male be killed after the eggs are laid a female can take over his work. That, however, cannot be the whole story. In aquaria females ready to lay but having no male present will build a bubble raft and lay their eggs, unfertilised. It has even been known for such a female to be helped by another female. In one instance an aquarium keeper kept a male and female apart, by sliding a sheet of glass between them. The male started to build a bubble raft one side of the glass and the female started one the other side. When the aquarist noticed this, and before he could move the glass, the female had laid her eggs under the raft and was trying to keep the male, on the other side of the glass, at bay.

class	**Pisces**
order	**Perciformes**
family	**Anabantidae**
genus & species	***Macropodus opercularis*** *others*

*Peculiar puzzling pseudid — the paradoxical frog has long been a zoological problem as it has no close relatives and so is difficult to classify. It is now put in its own family Pseudidae. This species, **Pseudis paradoxa** is the largest and best known paradoxical frog so called because of the disproportion in size between the tadpole and adult. It seems unbelievable that a 10½in. tadpole could metamorphose into a 1½in. froglet, but this is what happens.*

Paradoxical frog

These frogs are quite the reverse of other frogs: at metamorphosis they are several times smaller than their tadpoles.

In outward appearance the paradoxical frog looks like any ordinary frog. It is up to 3 in. long. Its hindfeet are webbed but the toes project beyond the webbing more than usual. Its colour varies among the usual greens and browns with darker spots and blotches but the hindlegs have a harlequin colouring of yellow and black.

There are several sub-species, the best known living on the island of Trinidad and in the northeastern area of South America and in part of the Amazon basin. Others are found in other parts of South America as far south as northern Argentina.

Stirring up mud

Paradoxical frogs are usually heard and not seen. They seldom come onto land and whenever they come to the surface of the water, they usually expose just their eyes or nostrils, and these are usually hidden among small water plants crowding the surface. The moment they are disturbed they dive. They have an added protection: their skin is unusually slippery so they are extremely hard to hold. They often make coughing grunts, however, almost like pigs.

Another peculiarity is that the toes have an extra joint, which gives them greater length, and this is linked with the method of feeding. They stir up the mud at the bottom of shallow lakes to find the small mud-dwelling invertebrates which they feed on. The first toe on each forefoot is opposable to the others, and it is used as a thumb for grasping food.

From giant to dwarf

The outstanding feature of this frog is the size of the tadpole, which may be 10½ in. long. When it changes into a froglet it shrinks to 1½ in. This is so unusual that the first scientists to study these frogs could not believe they belonged to the same species. When the tadpole shrinks by this tremendous amount all the internal organs must shrink proportionately, which was quite unheard of, so the adult frog was given one scientific name and the tadpole was given another. Only when the actual change from one to another had been observed was it realized that only one species was involved. In fact, the whole process was so puzzling that for a time there were several different scientific names for the different stages in the life-history. This is not the only time such a thing has happened, but it is very rare for there to be such a great reduction in size from the young or larval animal to the adult. It raises all manner of questions to which we do not yet know the answers; for example, how large the eggs are and whether they contain large quantities of yolk to feed the growing tadpole in its early stages. Another question to which we would like the answer is what advantage there can be in a tadpole growing so large then shrinking so much as it turns into a froglet.

Tadpoles to market

One reason why information on these frogs is so scanty is that they are difficult to find and therefore to keep in sufficient numbers in captivity to study them. Three individuals of one species were collected 100 years ago but there is no record of its having been seen since. Within the last few years, however, South American zoologists have been finding more of other species in areas south of the Amazon Basin, so more information may soon begin to trickle through. The tadpoles are easier to catch as they can be netted but even this apparently is not simple. The local Indians catch the tadpoles, as well as the adults, on hooks baited with grasshoppers, then sell them in the markets, and the tadpoles are particularly relished.

class	**Amphibia**
order	**Salientia**
family	**Pseudidae**
genus & species	*Pseudis paradoxa*

*Frog that shrinks as it grows, the paradoxical frog **Pseudis paradoxa**. An entirely aquatic frog, it lives in remote swamps and marshes where it is nearly invisible among the water weeds.*

Lorus & Margery Milne

Recorded distribution, although the frog probably has a wider unrecorded distribution.

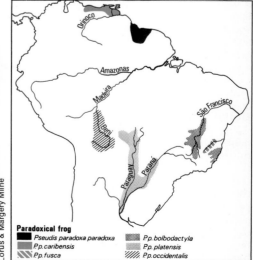

Paradoxical frog
Pseudis paradoxa paradoxa   P.p.bolbodactyla
P.p.caribensis   P.p.platensis
P.p.fusca   P.p.occidentalis

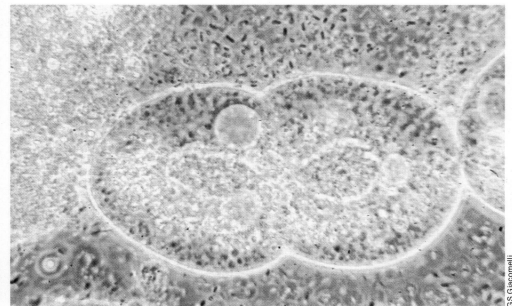

rows. These cilia are essentially the same as those that line our own breathing tubes and are associated with an orderly arrangement of structures just below the surface. The covering, or pellicle, is uniform except in the gullet and is made up of a lattice of polygons (usually hexagons) in close-packed rows just under the outer membrane. From the centre of each emerges one cilium, or two in **P. bursaria,** and at the base of each cilium is a cylindrical 'basal body'. To the left of each row of basal bodies, and connected to them, is a fine fibre which could be involved in coordinating the beating of the cilia. Many of the details are only revealed by electron microscopy and some of the earlier pictures, still being reproduced, are wrong. Amongst the cilia, just under

◁ *Binary fission in* **P. putrinum** *(× 1 000).*
▽ *Final stage, the furrow deepens (× 1 000).*

Paramecium

Nearly 6 000 species of ciliate Protista have been described. They are single-celled animals that typically, though not always, feed and swim by means of cilia. If any of these can be described as well-known, it is surely the much-studied slipper animalcule **Paramecium** *described by Christian Huygens as long ago as 1678 when microscopy was in its infancy. The largest are about $\frac{1}{3}$ mm long and the smallest about $\frac{1}{6}$ of that. There are about 10 species differing in size, shape and other details, but they are all elongated and more or less rounded at the ends and each has a wide shallow groove on its side, leading into a blind gullet. The general appearance is aptly expressed in the old popular name of 'slipper animal-cule'.* **Paramecium** *does not change its shape like* **Amoeba** *(p 34) except when squeezing through holes, and it swims with its short cilia arranged in longitudinal*

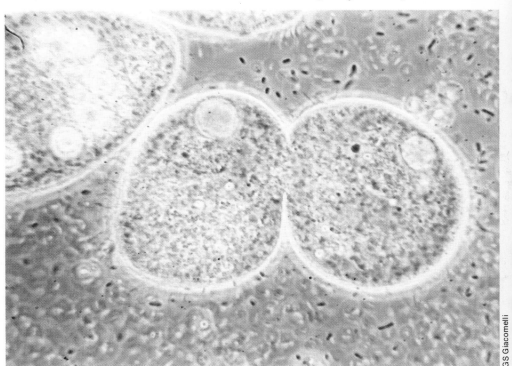

◁ *There are about 10 different species of* **Paramecium**, *2 of which are shown here (× 680).*

the surface, are little carrot-shaped bodies called trichocysts. Each one can discharge a rod $\frac{1}{50} - \frac{1}{25}$ mm long and ending in a sharp tip. It is not clear if these have any offensive or defensive function.

Inside the body there are two kinds of nucleus: a large 'macronucleus' and one or more small 'micronuclei'. For bailing out excess water, there are contractile vacuoles. In **P. caudatum,** the most widespread species, there is one at each end and the two contract alternately, but in other species there may be only one, or there may be as many as seven. Around each contractile vacuole are several radial canals which gradually fill with fluid, before discharging into the central vacuole, which collapses as it discharges its contents.

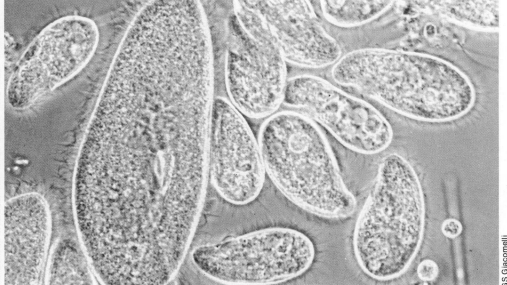

Trial-and-error navigation

In swimming the cilia of paramecium are co-ordinated, each beating a little in advance of the one behind it in the line, so that waves seem to pass from the front to the rear. As the body moves through the water it rotates anticlockwise, as seen from behind. When it meets an obstruction or an unfavourable chemical, the cilia beat in the opposite direction so the animal backs, then it turns and advances again, repeating this until a clear path is found. It is largely by this simple process of trial and error, that individuals tend to remain within the most favourable regions of their environment. Recently it has been shown that the reverse beating, when the front end is touched, is brought about by a temporary increase in the permeability of the surface to calcium ions and that stimulation of the rear end causes faster swimming by an increase in the permeability of the surface to potassium ions. The two reactions are accompanied by changes in the voltage across the surface of the animal.

Sometimes paramecium loses much of the organization of its body and surrounds itself with a thick membrane which becomes angular like a sand grain. This formation of a cyst probably aids dispersion and survival during a period of drought, but it has not often been seen.

Though some species occur in brackish water, paramecium lives mainly in fresh water, particularly where there is abundant decaying organic matter and its attendant bacteria. It is easily cultured in infusions of hay.

Temporary feeding organs

Paramecium eats bacteria, minute algae and smaller Protista wafted into the gullet by the cilia of the oral groove. The food is propelled down the gullet by more cilia, some of which are joined together side by side in rows to form 'undulating membranes'. At the bottom of the gullet, the food is collected in vacuoles in the cytoplasm. These tiny cavities then move into the cytoplasm and follow a definite path around the inside of the animal, finally discharging their indigestible contents at a point on the surface. If paramecium is fed on dried milk stained with a dye called congo red, the dye can be seen changing colour as the food vacuole moves around, showing that it is being subjected first to acid conditions and then alkaline, like food in our own digestive tracts. One species *P. bursaria* is coloured green by the cells of an alga *Chlorella* that lives inside it. Presumably, both organisms benefit from the partnership.

Sex at its simplest

Most of the time paramecium reproduces by division. The oral groove disappears, the nuclei divide, new contractile vacuoles form and a furrow appears across the middle of the body. In addition to this process of binary fission, which may happen 1–5 times a day, there occurs less frequently and often shortly after a depletion of food, a form of sexual reproduction usually referred to as conjugation. In *P. caudatum*, which has one of each kind of nucleus, the two individuals come together, joining in the regions of their oral grooves. The macronuclei break

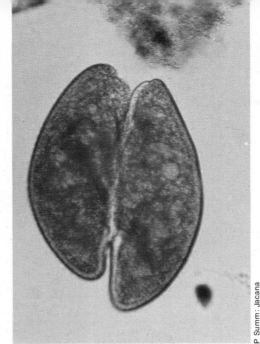

△ **Paramecium** *can reproduce in two ways, by an asexual method called binary fission, shown overleaf, in which the animal merely splits into two new individuals; or by a sexual method called conjugation, shown here, in which two animals come together and exchange nuclear materials so producing offspring with different hereditary constituents (× 650).*

down and in each individual the micronucleus divides into four. Of these four, three degenerate while the other divides again so each individual has 2 micronuclei, each with half the usual number of chromosomes. One of these migrates across into the other individual and there fuses with its opposite number. After this exchange of genetic material the two animals separate and the single effective nucleus in each divides again three times to give 8 nuclei

▽ *Pond water life, this is just a sample of what can be seen under the microscope. Among the freshwater algae and plankton are two paramecia,* **P. aurelia**. *They are easily distinguished by their characteristic slipper-shaped bodies. Free-swimming ciliates, they move by beating the cilia that cover their bodies (× 210).*

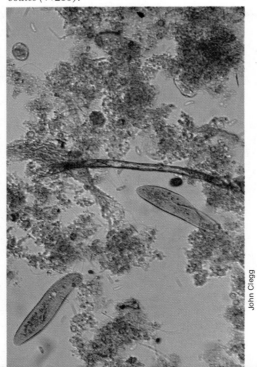

from which are formed the micro- and macronuclei of 4 new individuals. Sometimes self-fertilisation occurs: the 2 animals come together but do not exchange nuclei. In other instances, self-fertilisation takes place without mating. There are no distinct males and females, but each species occurs in a number of varieties and each variety in more than one 'mating type': conjugation can only occur between members of different mating types.

Killer strains

The nuclei in paramecium, as in other animals and plants, contain DNA, the complex chemical in which the information essential for form and function is coded, and which is transferred from one generation to the next during reproduction. In reproduction by binary fission the nucleus simply divides and there is no rearrangement of DNA, each offspring inheriting the same genetic information as the other. In sexual reproduction the exchange of half the genetic material allows for a rearrangement of DNA so the offspring vary slightly from the parents. This variation allows for evolution, the variants best suited to the environment surviving. In reproduction by binary fission, however, it is not just this genetic information that is passed to the progeny, but also the cytoplasm. Structures and characters can therefore be passed on from generation to generation other than in the nuclei. This is most dramatically seen in the phenomenon of 'killer' and 'sensitive' strains of *P. aurelia*. Certain strains, known as killers, contain kappa particles in their cytoplasm which release toxins into the water which cause members of other 'sensitive' strains to die in a few hours after showing such symptoms as paralysis, spinning and the appearance of a hump on the body. Sensitives can, however, be mated to killers without harm, provided suitable precautions are taken. If the pair remain together for a few minutes only, the two continue as before, killer and sensitive, but as a result of mating they acquire the same genetic make-up as far as the nuclei are concerned. If, however, the pair remain together for longer, for example half an hour, some cytoplasm is exchanged in addition to the nuclei and then both become killers. It is the kappa particles which pass over in the cytoplasm and are responsible for the effect, but just what the particles are is not clear, though they might be akin to viruses. They contain DNA and if destroyed by high temperatures or X-rays, killers are turned into sensitives. There is, however, more than one kind of killer race and, in some, a certain nuclear gene must be present if the particles are to be inherited.

phylum	**Protista**
class	**Ciliata**
subclass	**Holotricha**
order	**Hymenostomatida**
suborder	**Peniculina**
family	**Parameciidae**
genus	*Paramecium*

P Summ: Jacana

John Clegg

Parrakeet

Parrakeets are members of the parrot family, the most well known of which is the budgerigar (p 297). It is very difficult to give a definition of the name parrakeet, practically every book on birds, and certainly all dictionaries, differ in their views. Even the spelling of the name varies, from paroquet to parroquet, parakeet and parrakeet. Generally speaking, parrakeets can be defined as small brightly coloured parrots with long tails, but the name has been given to many genera and species in tropical America as well as in southern and southeast Asia and Australasia. Moreover, many of these have the alternative name of conure and rosella, the latter being a well known type of Australian parrot. To make matters worse many have more than one common name. The only hope of sorting out this confusion is to go to a book by AA Prestwich, the Secretary of the Avicultural Society of Great Britain, with the title 'I Name This Parrot . . .' In this the author has listed all the members of the parrot family, with their common names as well as their scientific names. The parrakeets he names belong to 23 genera, 68 species and 128 subspecies. In addition the parrakeets known as conures belong to 7 genera, 46 species and 63 sub-species. Since every species or sub-species of parrakeet has its own particular common name, this means in effect that there are 191 kinds of parrakeet known to aviculturalists, and since some have more than one common name this gives us about 300 names to play with.

New World parrakeets

Identification in this large group of colourful little parrots is especially confusing as they are not all closely related. The American parrakeets or conures, ranging from Mexico to Paraguay are related to the macaws, differing from them in having the lores—that is the space on each side of the head between the beak and the eye—feathered and in having a large swollen beak, not compressed as in the macaws. Also, the fourth feather of the wing is long and narrow and the nostrils are exposed. These parrakeets are usually some shade of green, yellow or orange with blue on the wings and red on the head and breast. The slender-billed parrakeet is another American species. It is 15 in. long and has pale green plumage with crimson on the forehead and around the eyes and lores and a faint patch on the abdomen. It lives in Chile, in large flocks numbering hundreds, and although it keeps mainly to the forests the slender-billed parrakeet comes out to attack crops from October to April, feeding on cereal crops and the roots of grass. The grey-breasted parrakeet is green with grey on the head, throat and breast. It is nearly

▷ *Looking over his shoulder from his lofty perch, a green ringnecked parrakeet.*

△ *Unruly chicks mob their parent for food. The torquoisine or western rock parrakeet nests in crevices among rocks.*
◁ *Multicoloured and broad-tailed, an eastern rosella* **Platycercus eximius**.
▽ *Uphill all the way, a blossom-headed parrakeet climbs with its feet and beak.*

foot long and ranges from Bolivia to
Argentine. There are several related species
in South America. Some of the smaller
American species are the green parrakeets,
—10 in. long, found in northern South
America and Central America.

Old World parrakeets

The Old World parrakeets are more nearly
related to the true parrots. They also are
mainly green. The ringnecked parrakeet
of Africa, up to 1½ ft long, has a graduated
tail in which the two central feathers are
long and narrow. It has a notch in the upper
half of the beak and a rose-coloured collar.
The Indian blossom-headed parrakeet, a
near relative, is more handsome still with
the head of the male tinged with red, plum-
coloured cheeks and a black collar.

Australian parrakeets

In southern Australia and Tasmania live
the grass parrakeets, of which the lovely
torquoisine is the best known. They are less
than a foot long and half of this is tail, and
are mainly green with blue in the wings and
blue sometimes in the tail. Normally they
move about in parties of 6—8 but will come
together in large flocks as particular seeds
ripen. There are related species in New
Zealand and some of the islands of the
southwest Pacific. Also in the southwest
Pacific, New Caledonia and the Loyalty
Islands are the ground parrakeets. These
are up to 14 in. long, and usually have a
crest. The New Caledonia crested parrakeet
has a crest of two black feathers tipped with
red but in others it is made up of six feathers
which are usually green.

The ground parrakeets of Australia are
of two kinds, long-tailed and short-tailed.
The first are sometimes spoken of as swamp
parrakeets because they tend to roost in
trees in swamps. They are distinguished by
the alternating dark and light bars on the
tail feathers which has led to a further
common name, pheasant-cuckoo. The long-
tailed ground parrakeets are about a foot
long of which half is tail. The general colour
is green, with orange on the forehead and
the body plumage mottled with bands of
black and yellow. The short-tailed parrakeets are nocturnal, coming out at sunset to
feed, and are sometimes called night parrakeets. They are now rare and there are
fears they may be on the way to extinction.

Topsy-turvy slumber

Parrakeets usually roost in trees and the
hanging parrakeets sleep head downwards
like bats. It seems that many more parrakeets than are realised sleep like this. One
is the lineolated parrakeet which feeds at
twilight. By day it is quiescent, freezing for
long periods at a time. At other times it
may perch lengthways along a branch,
nightjar fashion.

Vegetarians all

Some parrakeets go about in parties of half
a dozen or so, others in flocks of hundreds,
even thousands at times. They feed in trees
or on the ground, the proportion of time
given to each varying with the species. Their
food is mainly seeds, fruits, leaves and
flowers, and where they are numerous they
are apt to be a menace to crops.

Devoted families

Their nests are usually in hollows in trees
or among rocks, with no more than rotten
wood litter on which to lay their eggs. The
grey-breasted parrakeet is unusual in building a nest in the branches of a tree. Several
may nest close together, each nest made of
a mass of sticks, roofed in and with an
entrance to one side, high up in a tall tree.
Both female and male build the nest but
the hen alone incubates the eggs, which is
usual among parrakeets, and the male
attends her and guards the nest. The
number of eggs varies from 4 to 10 with the
species. Incubation usually lasts a month or
more, but may be much less in some species.
The chicks remain in the nest for 4—5
weeks, or as much as 10 weeks, both parents
feeding them.

Carolina parrakeet

A famous bird is the Carolina parrakeet. It
used to be seen in large numbers from South
Virginia to Texas and southeast to Florida. It is gaily coloured in green, rose,
yellow and white, but its raucous calling as
it flies about attracts attention as much as
its colour. It made a good pet, so it was in
demand as a cage bird, and its flesh was
good eating. Its feathers made good adorn-
ments for hats. At the same time it was destructive to fruit and cereal crops. If one
was shot its companions flew off but returned again and again to the spot, as if
trying to rescue it. By the 1880's it was
becoming rare. There may still be a few
Carolina parrakeets in some out-of-the-way
spot, but this is probably a vain hope.

class	Aves
order	Psittaciformes
family	Psittacidae
genera & species	*Aratinga* spp conures
	Brotogeris tirica
	green parrakeet
	Conuropsis carolinensis
	Carolina parrakeet
	Enicognathus leptorhynchus
	slender-billed parrakeet
	Eunymphicus cornutus
	crested parrakeet
	Geopsittacus occidentalis
	night parrakeet
	Myiopsitta monachus
	grey-breasted parrakeet
	Neophema pulchella
	torquoisine
	Pezoporus wallicus
	ground parrakeet
	Psittacula cyanocephala
	blossom-headed parrakeet
	P. krameri
	ringnecked parrakeet, others

▷ *What is in a name? According to the
dictionary a parrakeet is a small, especially
long-tailed, kind of parrot. Not altogether
very helpful but this bird with its technicolored
plumage perching coquettishly among the
sunshine-yellow Australian wattle is a crimson
parrakeet or rosella, perhaps better known as
Platycercus elegans to save confusion.*

Parrot profile. The African grey parrot, the most sought after and finest talking bird. The males make better mimics than the females. An admirable pet, it is reputed to have lived for 80 years in captivity. In the wild it travels in flocks feeding on all kinds of fruits and seeds testing them first with its fleshy tongue.

Parrot

Only about a third of the 315 members of the parrot family are given the name 'parrot'. The rest have other names, like cockatoos, parrakeets, lories, lorikeets, and macaws. Of the 107 parrots, 25 are amazons, stout-bodied American birds with mainly green plumage and short, square or rounded tails. One of the largest is the yellow-headed amazon which is 15 in. long. It is green except for the head and some blue and red in the wings. It ranges from Mexico to Brazil. One of the smallest is the white-fronted amazon which is 10 in. long. This amazon has a white forehead and bright red lores, and the male has a red wing patch. Another typical parrot is the African grey of the forests of tropical West and Central Africa. This bird has white cheeks and a red tail.

All members of the parrot family have large heads, short necks and strongly hooked beaks with the upper mandible longer than the lower and curving downwards. There is a broad cere at the base of the beak through which the nostrils open. Of the four toes on each foot two are directed forwards, two backwards. Powder down feathers are scattered through the plumage.

Raucous and agile

Parrots are essentially forest dwellers, travelling about in noisy flocks, the smaller parrots twittering, the larger uttering raucous shrieks and squawks. They climb about the trees, using beaks as well as feet, and, unlike most other birds, they can hold food with one foot. Their food is fruits, seeds and nuts. They seem to have a more highly developed sense of taste than most birds and will test food with their fleshy tongues before beginning to eat it.

Vocal mimics

The amazons and the African grey have been favourite pets, especially the latter, for centuries. This is because of their being able to 'talk', and the main interest in parrots lies in their vocal mimicry. A good 'talker' will imitate almost any sound from the songs of other birds and mechanical sounds to human speech. It will whistle tunes, sing short phrases from songs, laugh, cry, even call people by name: in short express itself vocally in a remarkably human way. An African grey has been recorded as imitating actions, using the foot to imitate its owner's use of the hand.

Where no wild parrots talk
The reputation of parrots as talkers has suffered in recent years from claims that budgerigars, and also mynahs, are superior in this respect. It is, however, doubtful whether there is much to choose between all three. It has also been repeatedly said that a parrot 'has no idea what it is saying'. In fact, careful study shows that parrots associate words and sounds with events and persons in much the same way, and to much the same degree, as a child of 2 years of age. Another assertion often made is that although such good mimics when tamed parrots never imitate sounds in the wild. This is hard to believe. A tame European jay is also a good talker and wild jays have been recorded as imitating the hoot of an owl. Such records are few but more would be made if people went out of their way to listen for them. It is highly likely that parrots also mimic sounds in the wild but that nobody has gone to the trouble of making the particular study needed to prove the point.

Cavity nesters
The breeding habits of parrots are fairly uniform. They usually nest in cavities in trees but some use burrows in the ground or crevices in rocks. A few Australian parrots dig holes in termite mounds. The nesting cavity is not lined; at best the eggs are laid on the powder of rotten wood or similar material. The eggs are nearly spherical, white and somewhat glossy. The clutch varies from 2 to 3 in the larger species to 10 in the smaller species. Few details are known except from parrots in aviaries, and the later events are best typified by what is known of the African grey. In this species the eggs are laid at intervals of 3 days, usually 4 eggs forming a clutch. Incubation, by the hen alone, lasts just over a month. The newly hatched chick is flesh-coloured with a light beak and light claws. The body soon becomes covered with a light down and the beak turns black after a few days. The hen broods the chicks, especially at night, for 2 months. Meanwhile, the male shares the feeding of the nestlings, by regurgitation. When first fledged the young parrot is like the parent except that the body feathers are a darker and softer grey, the tail feathers are a less vivid red and the eye is entirely black.

Birds as ventriloquists

When we consider how a bird's voice box is made the fact that they can imitate such a wide range of sounds is quite remarkable. Our larynx, with its vocal cords, is near the top of the windpipe. Air passing across the vocal cords makes them vibrate and the

sounds so produced are modified to form words and other modulated sounds by altering the position of the tongue and the teeth and by changing the shape of the cheeks and lips. In a bird the voice box or syrinx is at the base of the windpipe and it is worked by a dozen small muscles to produce all the modifications of the sounds. There are no cheeks or lips, in the sense of our pliable cheeks and lips, there are no teeth and the tongue is less mobile. So a bird must produce all the sounds it makes down in the throat. That is why a bird can sing, and often does, with the beak closed. It is also why a parrot can talk with its beak closed or nearly so. The ventriloquist does something like this, so producing the illusion that the voice is coming from somewhere else. The calls of many birds are often described as ventriloquial.

If we listen carefully to a ventriloquist we find his consonants are badly formed, although they sound right to the casual ear. It is the same with talking birds. This is underlined by the following story of a dog living in a house where there was a parrot. Whenever the dog rushed out into the garden, when it should not, its owner would whistle it or call it by name. The dog would

stop in its headlong rush and return to the house. If the dog rushed out when its owner was not there the parrot would whistle it or call it by name in what seemed a perfect imitation of the owner's whistle and voice. The dog, on hearing this, would raise its ears to listen, but without turning its head the slightest, then drop them again, meanwhile continuing its headlong run. It was as if the dog were saying to itself: 'Oh, it's only the parrot.' The assumption is that the dog, with its more discriminating ears,

*Looking down from his treetop perch is the blue-fronted amazon, **Amazona aestiva**. The amazon is another favourite pet, rivalling the African grey parrot for its famous talking ability.*

could *immediately* tell the difference between the owner's voice and the parrot's—which is more than human beings could do.

class	Aves
order	Psittaciformes
family	Psittacidae
genera & species	*Amazona albifrons* white-fronted amazon *A. ochrocephala* yellow-headed amazon *Psittacus erithacus* African grey others

Fowkein grey headed crow-tit, **Paradoxornis gularis**: *a grand name for such a small bird.*
Parrotbills are titlike birds with a deep, short, heavy bill like that of a parrot's.

Parrotbill

These small titlike birds are aptly named: they have a short, deep convex bill, like a parrot's. They are also known as crow tits or suthoras, and are classed by some ornithologists with the tits and by others with the babblers. Most of the 19 or 20 species live in the Orient, from India to China but not in the Malayan region. The reedling, however, ranges from China to Britain, where it breeds in a few areas mainly on the east coast. This species is usually called the bearded tit, the male having a prominent black stripe on each side of the bill like drooping moustaches. It is about 6½ in. long with a 3in. tail and in general appearance it looks rather like a small, long-tailed sparrow and can be confused with a long-tailed tit. The plumage is generally light brown with stripes of black, white and brown on the wings. The bill is yellow and the head lavender-grey. The female's plumage is dull by comparison.

A little larger than the reedling is Gould's parrotbill, 7 in. long, brown above and whitish below with black patches around the eyes. Blyth's parrotbill is only 4 in. long.

Agile acrobats

Parrotbills clamber agilely among grasses and bamboos in a very titlike manner pausing straddled between two stems. The habits of many of them are hardly known but most live in groups of up to 50, some-times in company with other birds such as tits and babblers, foraging in tall grasses, bamboos or the lower levels of trees, where their constant chattering gives them away. The reedling lives in reed beds where its presence is first betrayed by its high-pitched calls. Often all that will be seen of it is a glimpse of a small dark bird disappearing into the depths of the reeds but in the autumn especially small groups can be seen flying quite high over the reeds or foraging or roosting together among the reeds.

Stripping reeds

Parrotbills feed on insects, grass seeds and sometimes berries. During the breeding season reedlings feed on insects, caterpillars, mayflies and other insects, together with a few small snails. In the winter, however, they feed mainly on the seeds of reeds. The black-fronted parrotbill of Nepal, Burma, Thailand and China feeds on bamboo shoots as well as insects and the reedbed parrotbill feeds on insects and larvae that live inside the stems of reeds. The reedbed parrotbill is restricted to a 50 mile stretch of reeds along the Yangste Kiang, near its mouth. It searches for the holes made in the reeds by insects, then straddles the reed, inserting the tip of the upper mandible and tearing away strips of reed until the insects are exposed. The noise of the reeds being torn apart makes these parrotbills easy to find. They are also easy to approach.

Reed hammocks

Parrotbill nests are made of the leaves of grass or bamboo or strips torn off reeds woven tightly into cups around bamboo or stout grass stems and bound with cobwebs. Reedlings line their nests with the flowers of reeds and a few feathers. Both sexes help in building the nest but the male makes the lining. When he is displaying to the female he fluffs out his moustaches and erects a sort of crest on his head. The pair posture to each other with their tails spread and they fly up together with quivering wings. In captivity the female reedling has been seen roosting under the wing of the male. Reed-lings do not hold territories but search for their food over a large area of their reedbed.

The eggs, 2–4 for most parrotbills but 5–7 for reedlings, are incubated for nearly a fortnight by both parents. The chicks stay in the nest for about 10 days. There are 2, sometimes 3, broods a year.

Resilient reedling

The reedling is one of the rarest British breeding birds. At one time it was much more widespread in southern and eastern England, but cutting of reedbeds and drainage of marshes together with the sale of both the eggs and the birds has restricted the range of the reedling until it bred only in the reedbeds of Norfolk and Suffolk and a few other scattered localities. Since the nineteenth century the reedling has been safe from human persecution but it has suffered badly during hard winters. After the long winter of 1916/17 very few reedlings were left. Numbers increased again until 1939/40, when there was another severe winter. Again they recovered until the 6 weeks' hard weather early in 1947. So few reedlings survived the hard winter of 1947 that it was thought they would become extinct in Britain. In the summer of 1947 only 4 breeding pairs were recorded. Yet once again there was a remarkable recovery and 10 years later over 100 pairs were recorded in the counties of Norfolk and Suffolk. Since then numbers have continued to increase, with only temporary setbacks due to bad weather or flooding, and reedlings have now spread to other parts of the country. HE Axell, writing in *British Birds* for 1966, describes how groups of reedlings can be seen leaving the reedbeds after the breeding season. They spread across the country in search of new reedbeds where they can feed, and some stay there to breed. Reedlings have also crossed the North Sea from Holland, to reinforce those already in Britain.

The severe effects of hard winters on the reedling population is due to snow covering the reeds. In 1962-3 the population was not affected as much as in 1947 because although the frost was harder and lasted longer, there was less snow and the reedlings were able to find food.

class	**Aves**
order	**Passeriformes**
family	**Muscicapidae**
genera & species	***Panurus biarmicus*** *reedling* ***Paradoxornis flavirostris*** *Gould's parrotbill* **P. heudei** *reedbed parrotbill* **P. poliotis** *Blyth's parrotbill, others*

Colourful coral fish—parrotfish appear as blue-green patches moving around the tropical reefs on which they feed. With their parrot-like beaks (below) they bite off chunks of coral leaving distinct tooth impressions behind. Because of this feeding habit parrotfish slowly erode the reefs.

Parrotfish

These brilliantly coloured fishes do not in fact get their name from their gaudy colours but from their teeth, which are joined to form a 'parrot's beak' in the front of the mouth. Nobody knows how many species there are: 350 have been named but there are probably fewer than 80.

Parrotfishes live around tropical reefs. They vary in adult size, from 1—6 ft; a few have reached 12 ft. When merely cruising around they swim with their pectoral fins, using their tail only when they need to swim more quickly.

Herds of fishes

Parrotfishes of the genus *Sparisoma* may live solitary lives or they may come together in small groups without any social organisation. Some species of the genus *Scarus* move about in large schools of up to 40 when feeding, rather like herds of cattle. Because of this parrotfish are sometimes referred to as the 'cattle of the sea'. Often they are seen near the shore with their backs out of water. The schools are made up of fishes of about the same size, the smallest keeping together, and similarly with the medium and large sized individuals. In some species of *Scarus* the groups are smaller and are made up of several females with a mature male acting as leader, like cows with a bull. Should another male join the group he is chased away, the boss male sometimes trailing him 20 ft away for a distance of 100 yards before rejoining his harem.

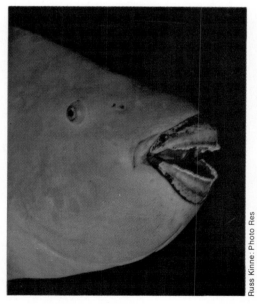

Different coloured sexes

For a long time parrotfishes were separated into species on the basis of colour. Then it was found that the same species could appear in different colours. Some species go through at least three different colour phases in the course of a lifetime. In others there is a marked difference between male and female. For example, *Scarus taeniopterus* is striped with orange and blue while *S. croicensis* is striped brown and white. Then it was realized they both belong to the same species, the first being the male, the second the female. This was tested by taking the female parrotfishes and injecting them with male sex hormones. *S. croicensis* so injected turned from brown and white striped to orange and blue striped. Where males and females are differently coloured the young fishes are coloured like the females. As they mature the females keep these colours but the males take on the colours of the mature males. Another change that can take place with age, in some parrotfishes, is that the males become bumpheaded. Instead of the forehead sloping it becomes a large bump, so that old males have heavy blunt snouts.

Homing by the sun

Some parrotfishes spend the nights under overhanging ledges of rock or in caves. When alarmed during the day they swim straight for their night quarters, in a direct line. Tests were made to see how they homed so accurately. First a net was hung in front of a cave and when the fishes were disturbed they swam straight for the net and continued trying to swim through it. When it was lifted they swam straight into the cave. The next test was to net some of the parrotfishes that were known always to swim in a south-easterly direction to their caves. They were then taken farther along the coast and put back into the sea. They immediately swam on a south-easterly course, to where there were no caves. When this experiment was repeated it was noticed that if a cloud passed across the sun the fish were temporarily lost. They swam about in different directions until the sun shone again, when they once more swam unerringly on a south-easterly course. Finally, the experiment was tried of blindfolding the fishes, by putting suction caps over their

*Properly dressed for the night, a sleeping parrotfish **Scarus guacamaia**. At night certain parrotfish reveal a remarkable phenomenon — they secrete a loose mucous envelope around themselves. This envelope may take half an hour to secrete and the same time to break out of at daylight.*

eyes. They swam in all directions, quite confused, but when the caps were removed they swam straight for their caves.

Eating hard tack

With their parrot-beak teeth they browse the eelgrass and seaweeds, often nipping pieces off the coral. In this way they erode the coral reefs. The pieces of coral swallowed are ground by flattened teeth in the throat. The undigested coral fragments are passed out and dropped in special places along the route the parrotfishes follow to and from their caves, accumulating in heaps. The sound they make when crunching the coral can be heard by anyone standing nearby.

Several kinds of courtship

It is not easy to generalize about the behaviour of parrotfish as they differ so much from one species to another. It is the same with their breeding habits. The eggs of *Scarus* species are elongated and oval, those of *Sparisoma* are spherical. In the one species *Sparisoma rubripinna* in which the spawning habits have been closely studied it was found that it bred all the year round but only in the afternoons. Then, a milling mass of fishes leaves its feeding ground close inshore

and assembles in depths of 65 – 70 ft, the mass keeping a few feet up from the bottom. Most of the fishes assembled there are males, so while the spawning is going on there is a preponderance of females inshore. Every now and then groups of 4 – 13 swim upwards from the main mass and circle rapidly around to release eggs and milt. There is, however, a second type of spawning in which a solitary male mates with a solitary female. The bulk of the eggs come from the group spawning, however. In another species a male and a female swim up to the surface, circling round each other as they go. As they get near the surface they are rotating round each other, and then they release a cloud of eggs and milt. The eggs of all species contain an oil drop, so they float near the surface. They range from $\frac{1}{25} - \frac{1}{10}$ in. diameter, and they hatch in a day, to release the usual fish larvae.

Nightdress or pyjamas?

When some parrotfishes *Scarus guacamaia* were kept in aquaria in 1954 they were seen as night fell to give out mucus, or slime, from glands in their skin. Later, other parrotfishes were seen to do the same thing.

The mucus formed a kind of loose shroud with an opening in the front guarded by a flap that allowed water in and a hole at the back which let it out. So the parrotfish can draw water in and pass it across its gills to breathe even while enclosed in what is almost a plastic cover. In the morning the parrotfish breaks out of its 'nightdress' and goes about its normal activities. When a parrotfish rests at night its breathing drops to a low rate. It is to all intents sleeping. The mucus envelope may be a way of preventing the gills silting up while the fish is resting on a sandy bottom, or it may be a protection from enemies. It is not known whether all parrotfishes do this, or even whether those species that have been seen to do it always do so. Whatever the situation is, a fish that wraps itself up for the night like this must be unique.

class	**Pisces**
order	**Perciformes**
family	**Scaridae**
genera	***Scarus***
	Sparisoma
	others

Partridge

The partridge — strictly the grey partridge — is famous as a game-bird on arable land in Europe and southwest Asia. There are, however, several score of related species in Europe, Asia and Africa, including tree partridges, wood partridges and bamboo partridges.

The common or grey partridge is plump, with a rounded body 1 ft long, a short beak and short tail. Its weight is around 1 lb. Its plumage is generally brownish with grey and white markings. The back of the male is brown streaked with buff and white. The neck is grey and the head orange-brown. The colours, however, are somewhat variable. The distinctive markings are on the front: the grey throat and upper breast and the chestnut horseshoe on the pale grey lower breast. The bill and legs are bluish grey. The head of the female is more streaked than in the male and the horseshoe is smaller, often absent altogether. The red-legged partridge is slightly larger, 13½ in. long, and can be distinguished from the common partridge at close quarters by the white cheeks and throat bordered by a black band, the flanks barred with black, white and chestnut, and the red bill and legs.

The common partridge, with its several subspecies, ranges across Europe into western Asia, and it has become acclimatized in the United States and Canada. The red-legged partridge is native to southwest Europe but has been introduced into several more northerly countries in Europe.

The 16 species of tree partridges **Arborophila**, living in forests from eastern India to southern China and Malaya, are beautifully marked, as are the five species of wood partridges of Malaya to Borneo. The three species of bamboo partridges, of southern China to Burma and Vietnam, have long tails and spurs, and are more like pheasants.

Vegetarian bird

Partridges are fairly inactive most of the day although they may feed a little. Their main feeding periods are early morning and in the evening. Their food is 97% plant material, with seeds, young shoots, some roots and fallen berries and occasionally root crops like turnip and beet. The 3% insects eaten are mainly ants and their pupae.

Large clutches

The nest, a scrape in the ground lined with dry grass and dead leaves, is built among tall herbage or under bushes or other cover. The eggs, 8–23 in a clutch, are laid in April or May at intervals of 24–36 hours. The somewhat pear-shaped eggs of the common partridge are olive brown, while those of the red-legged partridge are yellowish-white to pale yellowish-brown with a few reddish spots. The common partridge covers her eggs with grass until the clutch is complete, but the red-legged leaves hers uncovered. Incubation by the female begins only when the clutch is complete, all eggs hatching within a few hours, after a period of 23–25 days. The chicks begin to flutter when 10 days old and fly at 16 days.

Nest robbed

Little is known in precise detail about enemies but it is reasonable to assume that partridges have their nests robbed and their eggs and chicks taken by ground predators as well as by birds, such as crows, rooks and magpies. Any bird that lays up to 20 eggs or more in a clutch can be assumed to have numerous enemies or they would soon overrun their habitat.

Military parades

From time to time people report seeing birds following each other in orderly line across the ground, usually in threes or other low numbers. The birds keep in line, evenly spaced, and having gone so far, disperse or turn about and walk back with the same military precision. Hoopoes have been seen to do this. Blackbirds often do, and other species of birds have also been seen to carry out these seemingly senseless evolutions. We have a possible clue to these strange antics in the behaviour of partridges in spring. The males go in for automatonized chasing in which one chases the other, then they turn round and the chaser becomes the chased. They keep a regular distance, both move at the same speed, and they turn as on a word of command. Sometimes they turn at shorter and shorter intervals until they touch, then they fight. On rare occasions three have been seen to indulge in this ritualized chasing along a stretch of 50 yards or so.

Party life

The common partridge usually walks with its neck drawn into its shoulders but when suspicious it stretches up its neck to keep watch, and then runs for cover. It lives in small parties, or coveys, except in the breeding season. When suddenly startled, the covey rises with a whirring of wings, and flies strongly and swiftly, but not for long, typically hedge-hopping. The red-legged partridge seems more restless; it moves more quickly, runs rather than flies when alarmed, and the covey scatters instead of keeping close together like the common partridge coveys. The coveys are made up of parents and young which keep together until the next breeding season. Several coveys of common partridges may join for roosting among the ground vegetation.

△ *Distinctive front of a common partridge.*
Previous page: Chukar partridge A. graeca.

There is some disagreement as to whether the birds, which form a circle when they roost, turn their heads inwards or outwards, but most reports speak of them sleeping with heads outwards, which seems the most natural. Some observers report seeing them with heads turned inwards, which would seem to have disadvantages should the birds need to make a quick getaway. Evidence one way or the other is hard to get and depends more than anything else on the pattern of the droppings. The chief call of a common partridge is a hoarse note, like a key being turned in a rusty lock. That of the red-legged partridge is a chack-chack-chack, like a steam engine.

class	**Aves**
order	**Galliformes**
family	**Phasianidae**
genera & species	*Alectoris rufa* red-legged partridge *Perdix perdix* common partridge

◁ *Handsome male red-legged partridge stands on guard while his mate sits hidden on the nest.*

Pastoral ant

The pastoral ants do not represent a natural classification but an ecological grouping of those species of ants which indulge in a form of husbandry. It has long been known that some species of ants regularly visit aphides, otherwise known as greenfly or blackfly (p 69) to take the honeydew from them. The story is so well known today that there must be few people who have not heard it. Yet, as we shall see later, it was once thought unbelievable. What is not so well known is that not only do ants 'milk' the aphides, much as we milk cows, but they tend, herd and shepherd them, much as livestock are cared for by human herdsmen. Moreover, other insects such as scale insects, leafhoppers and the caterpillars of many butterflies, are also used by ants because they give out either honeydew or some other sweet fluid. Part of the story has already been given under blues (p 245). The caterpillars of these butterflies are taken into their nests by ants solely for the sake of the sweet fluid they give out. Here we shall deal with some of the more remarkable ways in which ants make sure of a continual supply of honeydew from aphides.

Honey farms

'Aphid farms' are described on page 71. In these the ants shepherd the aphides to the more tender parts of the plant, so the improved 'pasture' results in the aphides giving a greater supply of honeydew. Some ants take honeydew only when they happen to come across aphides. In others, it is less haphazard and when the ant strokes an aphid with its antennae the aphid responds by increasing the flow of honeydew. Further, some aphides have a special structure, a sort of drinking vessel, into which the honeydew flows and from which the ant can drink. The link between the two insects is so close that if the aphides are threatened the ants will pick them up and carry them away to safety. Some ants, it is said, take the aphides into their underground nests for the night and bring them out again the following morning, placing them back on the leaves from which they were taken the previous evening.

Battery farming

It is not only green leaves that serve as pasture. There are ants which take aphides underground, excavating cavities for them, to feed on the sap in roots. Others build special shelters on the stems of plants which may be just roofs or may be complete 'stables', entirely enclosing the aphides. Various materials may be used; earth is made into a cement with saliva, chewed plant fibres make a form of paper, known as carton. This paper is manufactured in much the same way that wasps make their paper nests. The making of carton is a feature more especially of certain tree ants *Crematogaster*, which also use it for making brood chambers in their nests for their own eggs and larvae.

A big occasion — winged males and females of **Camponotus ligniperda** *engage in a nuptial dance surrounded by other members of the colony.*

Klaus Paysan

Egg marketing

Some ants carry their pastoral activities a stage further. In the autumn aphides lay their eggs on the stems of shrubs. They remain there all winter, hatching the following spring. Not all the eggs survive because of the many predators, including some of the small insectivorous birds that are forever searching the crevices in the bark of trees and shrubs for anything edible. There are, however, some species of ants which in autumn, when the aphides are laying their eggs, carry these eggs down into deep underground nests, tending them throughout the winter. Then, when they hatch in the spring the ants carry the larvae up above ground and place them on plants to feed. They may place them first on one plant then on another as the spring succession of green shoots unfolds, so providing them with the best possible pastures.

Over-grazing

In spring the foliage of a climbing rose, a peach tree or other shrub or tree sometimes suddenly becomes infested with aphides. One day it is, to all intents clean, then two or three days later it is covered with these plant lice. In England, at least, it is not unusual to hear someone say: 'Look how the blight has struck this rose (peach or plum tree, as the case may be). It came in with the east wind (or the southwest wind, or whatever wind had been blowing).' These visitations are partly the results of the high rate of reproduction of the aphides, so one day they are too few to be noticeable, then 2–3 days later they are everywhere on the bush or shrub and the leaves are curling. In some instances, the original cause may be pastoral ants carrying the aphides and planting them there. This is especially true of young peach trees, and if we look carefully we shall see the ants streaming up and down the stem and along the branches, among the hordes of aphides.

The ant-aphid relationship may have begun by the ant mistaking the aphid's abdomen and back legs for the head and antennae of a fellow ant.

W Harstrick:Photo Res

A North American ant *Lasius americana* is notorious for tending the aphid *Anuraphis maidi-ridicis*, which feeds on the roots of cotton and corn. The ant looks after the aphid eggs in winter and plants the young aphides on the crop in spring. But for the ants, the aphides in some places probably would not survive the winter, or would do so in such small numbers as to be negligible. As it is, the intervention of the ants can sometimes result in serious damage to the crop.

'Ant-cows'

Linnaeus, the Swedish botanist, 200 years ago named the aphides 'ant-cows' and spoke of ants milking them. A century later we find William Kirby and William Spence, in their famous *Introduction to Entomology,* speaking about this in curious terms. Having described the slave-making ants they say: 'That ants should have their *milch cattle* is as extraordinary as that they should have slaves. Here, perhaps, you may again feel a fit of incredulity shake you:—but the evidence for the fact I am now stating being abundant and satisfactory, I flatter myself it will not shake you long.' The subject was more fully studied later in the 19th century by Sir John Lubbock (later Lord Avebury) and the incredulous became fully accepted. Some writers have used the name dairying ants, others pastoral ants, and Alexander B and Elsie B Klots, in their *Living Insects of the World,* published in 1959, comment that no human could take more care of his domesticated stock than these ants do of their aphid 'cattle'.

phylum	**Arthropoda**
class	**Insecta**
order	**Hymenoptera**

Patas monkey

A large red monkey related to the guenons (p 975), the patas monkey, also called the hussar or military monkey, lives on the open plains. It is built like a greyhound, with a deep chest, supple back and long legs for running fast, and the fingers and toes are short. The males are twice the size of females. An adult male may be 3 ft long in head and body with a tail nearly as long and it weighs 28 lb. A female will weigh only 11–15 lb. Males are much more brightly coloured than females: the rump and back of the hindlegs are white, standing out against the red body colour. In the female the light areas are fawn. The face is whitish with short cheek-whiskers brushed back; the nose is often blue.

Patas monkeys are found throughout the savannah zone, especially in areas of long grass, from West Africa to as far east as the Sudan, Uganda, and northwestern Kenya. Being able to tolerate very dry conditions, they have extended their range into Air, in the southern Sahara.

One-man troops

A troop of patas monkeys is led by one of the females. The male, who plays no part in determining its movements, is really almost a hanger-on. The monkeys live in small troops, of 6–30, in which there is only one adult male, the males being intolerant of each other in the presence of females. Surplus adult males live alone or in bachelor bands in outlying areas. When two troops meet, which is rare, the larger one generally chases away the smaller. It is possible that an individual male from the bachelor band sometimes proves stronger than the male in a troop and so takes his place. When the troop male meets a strange patas or troop of them, he utters a series of deep barks which rally the females, one of which may give chase.

The troop has a home range of up to 20 sq miles in the semi-arid savannah. Unlike baboons, the other open-country African monkeys, patas monkeys have no 'core areas' in their range, all of the home range being utilised equally. There are no favourite sleeping-trees—at night the troop roosts where it is, nearly every individual occupying a separate tree, so the troop is widely scattered. During the day the troop wanders about over its home range, covering a distance of not less than a ¼ mile in a day—and sometimes nearly 8 miles, feeding in the morning and again in the evening, and resting during the heat of the day.

Quarrels over mushrooms

Patas eat much grass; also the fruit pulp of the tamarind, the fruit of several other trees, as well as seeds, and berries. They pluck these with their hands, not with their mouths, and they often stand on their hindlegs to pull down seeds from tall grass or low bushes. They cannot uproot grasses or dig for roots and tubers as the stronger baboons do. Patas are fond of mushrooms, especially the big *Lepiota*, and it is over these favoured items that some of the few quarrels occur in patas societies. The adult male or the larger females, including those with infants, do not hesitate to snatch pieces from others or chase them away from the mushroom patch. They may sit feeding on the mushrooms for as much as 20 minutes before passing to another source of food.

Happy childhood

Females come into season every 30 days or so. When mating is over, the female stays with the male, and after a while they mate again. Births take place throughout the year but there is a peak in the dry season, between December and February. The infant at first clings to its mother's belly, but gradually becomes independent. At no time does it ride on its mother's back, like the infant baboon. Infants spend most of their time playing: chasing and wrestling, and do so up to one year of age.

Male acts as a lure

Lions, leopards, hyenas, jackals, wild dogs, pythons, crocodiles and eagles probably all

knit troop in which there are usually several males who can band together against a potential predator. The patas monkeys' reaction is to flee, while the only male in the troop makes a diversion. Because they are weaker animals and subject to greater dangers from enemies, patas monkeys use a much larger home range—20 square miles as against 3½ for baboons—over which they wander widely and more freely. Patas monkeys very rarely come to drink at standing water, and have never been seen to drink from rivers, whereas baboons do both. Presumably it is too dangerous for patas to do so, so they have to get all their moisture from their food and from dew. Male baboons are very aggressive and frequently quarrel. Patas monkeys, on the other hand, rarely quarrel and never fight within the troop, and when two troops meet it is the females that initiate any chasing.

There is a difference even in the way the infants play. Young baboons play mostly in the morning and evening, keeping near the sleeping trees, whereas young patas play towards midday when it is hot and predators, as well as their parents, lie in the

Three of a troop of patas monkeys put their heads down and drink while the others keep watch.

take their toll of the patas monkeys. It is here that the male of the troop comes into his own. Because he is not dangerous and fearsome like a baboon, the male patas makes a diversionary display. He bounces noisily on bushes and trees and runs away fast through the grass, drawing attention away from the females and young who stand hidden in the long grass or flee silently. Not only does the male make himself conspicuous by his behaviour, he is also conspicuously coloured, and he has to rely on his greyhound build to carry him swiftly through the grass.

He also acts as a watchdog. He is the first to reconnoitre an area before the troop goes in and he often stands upright, using his tail as an extra support like a shooting stick, to see over the grass.

Living close to danger

Although patas and baboons live in the same open country, their way of life is markedly different. Baboons live in a close-

shade. The mother patas is much more possessive than the mother baboon who lets other females and even males play with and handle her infant. The mother patas is entirely responsible for her infant's safety and cannot depend, as the mother baboon does, on having the whole troop to help her defend her infant.

Finally, and perhaps most striking of all, the patas troop is very silent. Ronald Hall, who studied these monkeys in the wild, records he heard about 50 vocalisations from a baboon troop every day and only two from a patas group. The moral seems obvious: if you have nothing with which to fight, it is best to keep quiet.

class	**Mammalia**
order	**Primates**
family	**Cercopithecidae**
genus & species	***Erythrocebus patas***

Peafowl

There are three species of peafowl, the blue or Indian, the green, which lives farther east, from Burma to Java, and the Congo peacock. The first has been kept in semi-domestication for over 2000 years and is better known as the peacock and peahen.

Because the blue or common peacock, of India and Ceylon, is so well known it hardly needs description. We need only stress its outstanding features; the head and neck are a glorious blue, relieved only by white patches, one above and one below the eye. The head bears a crest made of a bunch of divergent brush-like feathers tipped with blue. The body is drab by comparison; greyish barred with brown on the back, and brown wings and under-side. The real beauty of the peacock is in its train, usually called its tail although made up of greatly elongated tail coverts, not of tail feathers. Including its train a peacock measures up to 7½ ft long, of which nearly two-thirds is train. The peahen is less showy, her plumage more brownish and she lacks the train.

Both male and female of the green pea-fowl are green with bronze mottlings from the crest to the tail. The wings are turquoise and black, and the whole has a metallic appearance. The crest is smaller than in the common peacock. Albino, pied and black-shouldered mutations have appeared but these are soon lost by cross-ing with pure stock. Blue and green hybridize in captivity, the offspring being like the blue parents.

The Congo peacock, not discovered until 1936, lives in deep forests. The male is blue and green with a short broad tail, a patch of naked red skin on the neck and a double crest of black and white. The female is chestnut and coppery green.

△ An eye-spot with its shimmering colours.

◁ Splendidly useless. Magnificent train of blue peacock seems to have little effect on the hen.

Very regular habits

Peacocks feed on the ground and roost in the trees bugling loudly in the late afternoon as they go up branch by branch. Their loud screeching call can be heard intermittently after dark also. Where, in the wild state, they are persecuted, they soon react by keeping out of sight in the forests, and when they do so their plumage serves as effective camouflage. Where they are undisturbed they readily live around human settlements, attaching themselves to buildings. This is a marked feature of their behaviour in semi-domestication and it is linked with an unusual regularity in their habits generally. Peafowl not only keep to the same roost, visit the same feeding grounds or sunbathing places, regularly day after day, but the male also has a chosen place for displaying.

Ring of peacocks

One unusual piece of behaviour can be compared with that of male partridges. Peafowl have been seen to chase one another in circles around a bush or a clump of bamboo. This is most often done by birds in their second year but occasionally an adult hen will join in. Exceptionally an adult peacock will join in when his train has moulted. The birds run with their necks stretched parallel to the ground, sometimes one overtaking another, and they always travel anti-clockwise. After running round in circles for a while, they will all stop suddenly and simply wander away.

Nothing edible refused

Peafowl eat grain and seeds, fruits, insects and, in gardens, bread and other scraps. They seem to be ready to try almost anything edible, plant or animal, and peacocks have been seen to kill and eat snakes and also mice. They will, like the barnyard chicken, snap flies from the air or chase butterflies. A clue to their omnivorous feeding and to other of their features is given in the words of an early 19th-century writer: 'I find nothing that is either pleasing or deserving of attention, except a beautiful plumage. Its voice is a loud and dis-

gusting scream, and the damage it does to plants in our gardens is scarcely compensated by its elegant appearance there.'

The fan dance

The peacock's train is described in the ornithological literature as made up of elongated tail coverts, partly de-composed and tipped with ocelli, or eye-spots. The 'de-composition' means the barbules of the feathers do not interlock, having lost their hooks, making them look ragged. Their greenish shimmering colours and the beauty of the eye-spots when the train is spread in a fan offsets such derogatory remarks. The peacock shows off his fan to the peahen or to any other passing bird, even to humans and he sometimes wheels around and displays the back view of the fan which is more drab. He often postures and struts while showing off but in fact this is often due to the need to keep his balance as the wind catches this enormous fan. From time to time he quivers the fan or rattles its quills. The effect is largely lost on the 4–5 hens in his harem but eventually mating takes place. The display is not the prerogative of the peacock alone; the peahen, even the peachicks, will posture with their undersized tail coverts spread.

Where there are many ground predators the nest may be built in a tree, but more usually it is a shallow scrape in the ground in which 8–20 eggs are laid, during January to March. The hen feeds the chicks from her beak, at which the chicks instinctively peck. In domestication peafowl eggs are sometimes put under barnyard hens. The chicks from these have to learn to pick up food from the ground. Orphaned chicks placed in the care of an immature peahen will peck at her beak. This stimulates her, after a while, to feed them, and she will later take them under her wings.

Varying fortunes

The peafowl is venerated in parts of its native range. Elsewhere it is killed for food. Alexander the Great introduced it to the Ancient Greeks who made it sacred to Hera, queen of the heavens. It later became associated with Juno, Hera's Latin counterpart, as a regal bird but by the first century BC roast peacock had become fashionable at banquets and a symbol of extravagant feasting. The fashion spread north and west into mediaeval Europe. Peacock's feathers, by contrast, have at all times been prized and Olaus Magnus tells us that in 17th-century Scandinavia the birds were reared solely for their aesthetic value, as indeed they are today, being ornamental additions to many private and public gardens.

◁ *Behind the scenes: a peacock viewed from behind. As the curtain rises, the straight lines of the tail coverts spread out fan-wise. The barbules of these coverts do not interlock as they have lost their hooks, and this makes them look very ragged, especially at the ends.*

▷ *Peacocks by moonlight. With their long flowing silhouettes etched against the sky, they are a beautiful and romantic sight, especially when they do not ruin it with their loud screeching calls.*

Proud as a peacock

The peacock has long been a symbol of vanity. Whose vanity it was supposed to epitomise, its own or that of human beings who gaze upon it, is an open question. From the frequency with which we speak of people who strut and give themselves airs as being 'proud as a peacock' the likelihood is that we see reflected in the peacock's display some of our own vanity. This is a little unfair on a bird that merely indulges in a stereotyped courtship display under the influence of gonadotrophic hormones. Courtship displays are not peculiar to birds but they reach their highest expression in them. There are very few species of birds in which the males do not use elaborate display in the breeding season. The main difference between them and a peacock is that the latter has more to display. But even a crow or a rook, black all over — except when the blue or purple iridescence shows up at close quarters — is in its way as magnificent as any peacock when displaying.

class	**Aves**
order	**Galliformes**
family	**Phasianidae**
genera & species	***Afropavo congensis*** *Congo peacock* ***Pavo cristatus*** *common peafowl* ***P. muticus*** *green peafowl*

Pearlfish

These fishes were so named because they are often found embalmed in pearls in oyster shells, and also because their bodies are transparent with a pearly lustre. They are familiar to biology students as **Fierasfer,** *a fish that lives in the body of a sea-cucumber. The two dozen species of pearlfishes are thin and eel-like, usually only a few inches long. The longest is 12 in. They have scaleless, rounded bodies or are compressed from side to side. The tail tapers almost to a point. The dorsal fin starts just behind the head and continues round the tail to join the long anal fin. The pectoral fins are very small and there are no pelvic fins. The body is transparent so the internal organs and*

normally uses a sea-cucumber for a host will enter an artificial sea-cucumber so long as water is flowing out of it and some mucus from a live sea-cucumber has been added to the aquarium water. A sea-cucumber breathes by drawing water in through its vent, passing it through its gills, and then driving it out again. Young pearlfishes swim in headfirst, the head keeping the vent open while the tail is being inserted. Should the sea-cucumber try to close its vent before the fish is in, a pearlfish may twist its long tail like a corkscrew to insinuate itself inside. More than one pearlfish may live in the same sea-cucumber, and as many as seven have been seen to enter, one after the other.

Vipers in the sea-cucumber bosom

For the most part pearlfishes shelter by day and come out at night to feed on copepods, small shrimps, small crabs and probably

survive outside. When it has reached a length of 8 in. the tenuis larva changes to a juvenile, which is much shorter, and can leave its host for a while each day, but it feeds on the gills and the reproductive organs of the sea-cucumber. The fourth and last stage is the adult. The shelter of the sea-cucumber is still necessary but when older it is used only as a temporary day refuge.

Larvae live dangerously

Nothing definite is known about their enemies, but once the pearlfishes have started to shelter, whether in rock crevices or in living animals, their daily risks must be much reduced. No doubt some fall prey to predatory fishes when they are feeding, but these losses are probably small. The heaviest mortality is almost certainly during the planktonic larval stage.

▽ *Pearlfish at its front door — a sea cucumber.*

William M Stephens

the backbone are visible.

Pearlfishes live mainly in tropical and subtropical seas, although a few species occur in temperate seas. They inhabit shallow water down to depths of 600 ft.

Most remarkable partnership

Adult pearlfish shelter in cracks and crevices in rocks, inside the shells of bivalve molluscs or inside the bodies of sea-squirts, sea-urchins, starfishes and sea-cucumbers. Most of them come out to feed but a few live permanently and parasitically inside the body of another animal. Sometimes pearl-fishes are caught in nets which suggests that some of them may spend a larger proportion of their time swimming freely than hiding in crevices. Some species of pearl-fishes will shelter in a variety of hosts, like *Carapus homei,* of the Malay Archipelago, which will readily go into a starfish, sea-urchin, clam or other animal, whereas *C. bermudensis* of the Caribbean uses only three species of sea-cucumber. These spend only part of their time within the host, but others, such as *C. acus* of the Mediterranean, live permanently in it.

Experiments show that a pearlfish that

other small invertebrates. The parasitic species feed on the reproductive organs of their hosts, and possibly other of their internal organs. This may not be as bad for the sea-cucumbers as it appears because they have the habit of casting out their internal organs in moments of crisis and growing a new set. So presumably they can re-grow any parts that are nibbled away.

Packets of eggs

The eggs are laid in sticky, roughly cylindrical masses, 2–3 in. long. After this each fish passes through four stages, with changes at each stage in the shape of the body, colour and behaviour. In the Mediterranean pearlfish the first or vexillifer larva is very slender and has a long lobe on its back. This is not a fin but a flag-like outgrowth of the body (*vexillifer* means a standard-bearer). As the larva grows in size the 'flag' becomes small, disappearing when the baby fish is $2\frac{1}{2}$ in. long. All this time it has lived in the plankton. The next stage, the tenuis, or slender larva, has a larger head relative to the rest of the body and it begins to grow long teeth. It must now enter a sea-cucumber. It cannot change from one sea-cucumber to another and it cannot

Patchy distribution

Although pearlfishes are found in all tropical and subtropical seas their distribution seems to be patchy, even in localities where there are plenty of sea-cucumbers. In one study off Hawaii, of 122 sea-cucumbers examined only 2 had a pearlfish inside. Several hundred examined off the Marshall Islands, in the South Pacific, yielded only one fish, and off Florida 100 sea-cucumbers yielded only three pearlfishes. William M Stephens reports that after collecting hundreds of sea-cucumbers off Miami, in some places half of them had pearlfishes inside while in other places only 2 in every 100 contained fishes, and off the Bahamas 1 in every 3 had a fish inside.

class	**Pisces**
order	**Gadiformes**
family	**Carapidae**
genus & species	***Carapus acus*** ***C. bermudensis*** ***C. homei*** *others*

Peccary

Peccaries are the South American equivalent of the Old World wild pigs, which superficially they resemble. They are smaller than the true pigs, however, and differ in other important details so they are placed in a separate family, the Tayassuidae.

Peccaries have long slim legs and small hooves and there are only three toes on the hindfeet, not four as in true pigs. The tail is vestigial and the body is covered with thick bristly hairs, which form a slight mane on the neck. When the peccary is agitated the hairs on the spine are raised, exposing a scent gland on the lower back. This gives out an unpleasant musky odour detectable at some distance. Peccaries have more complex stomachs and fewer teeth than true pigs, and their short sharp upper tusks grow downwards instead of upwards.

There are two species: the collared peccary which is found in deserts, woodland and rain forests from the southern borders of the United States to Argentina; and the white-lipped peccary, ranging from Paraguay to Mexico, which is less well-known as it lives deep in the tropical rain forests that cover much of this area.

*The collared peccary is the smaller, standing 20 in. at the shoulder with a maximum length of about 37 in. and it weighs up to 65 lb. The coarse hair is black mixed with white, so the effect is greyish, and it owes its name to the narrow semi-circular collar of lighter hair on the shoulders. Alternative names are musk hog or javelina—the Spanish **javeline** means spear—descriptive of its spear-like tusks.*

The white-lipped peccary is dark reddish brown to black in colour with, as the name suggests, an area of white round the mouth. It can be as much as 41 in. long and stands 24 in. at the shoulder.

John Tashjian at Tuxtla Gutierrer Zoo

A white-lipped peccary follows its nose. Peccaries have an extremely keen sense of smell and can even locate food an inch or so under the ground. Their senses of sight and hearing, on the other hand, are relatively weak. Peccaries have coarse, bristly hair, long slim legs and small hooves.

Safety in numbers

The speed and agility of peccaries, who move with a fast running gait when pursued, combined with a group defence system, protect them from dogs, coyotes and even bobcats. Although not normally aggressive to humans, an entire herd may counter-attack if one member of it is wounded or chased. They are hunted for their hides and meat, and when brought to bay the herds are described as standing in close formation, champing their tusks and making determined charges at their hunters.

Both species are gregarious, but whereas the collared peccary associates in groups of 5–15, the herds of the white-lipped peccary are much larger, being up to 100 or more. Males and females of all ages are found in these groups, which do not appear to move over large areas: the territorial range of the collared peccary for example is usually only about 3 miles.

The herds have no apparent leader and it has been suggested that the musk gland plays an important part in co-ordinating group movements. Peccaries of the same herd practise mutual grooming, in the course of which they rub their throats and shoulders on each other's musk glands, a habit known as 'smell-sharing behaviour'. In the normal course of events, secretions from these glands will also be transferred to low branches or bushes along paths frequented by the herds, thus making the home territory as well as fellow-members of a herd instantly recognisable by smell to each individual.

Grub up!

Peccaries are most active in the cooler hours of the day, and at night. Their usual resting place is in a thicket or under a large boulder, or they will readily take to the abandoned burrows of other animals. Their eyesight is not good and their hearing only fair but they have a keen sense of smell, being able for instance to locate an edible bulb an inch or so under the ground. The collared peccary is mainly vegetarian and uses its pig-like snout to root for fruit, berries and bulbs. It will, however, also eat grubs, occasionally small vertebrates and even

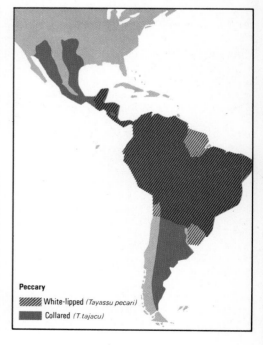

Peccary

White-lipped *(Tayassu pecari)*

Collared *(T. tajacu)*

snakes; it appears to be immune to rattle-snake venom. The white-lipped peccary is more omnivorous, living on carrion, worms and insects as well as on a variety of fruits and roots, and is reputed to hunt larger prey. It is never far from running water.

Short infancy

Very little is known of the breeding habits of the white-lipped peccary, but in the collared species the litter consists of 1—4, normally 2, young, and many females breed twice in the same year. Gestation is variously given as 112—116 and 142—148 days. The young are born in a burrow, hollow log or cave. Their colour is quite different from an adult's, being reddish with a dark stripe down the back. They are able to run when a few hours old and are weaned at 6—8 weeks. Life expectancy is up to 20 years.

You scratch my back . . .

Peccaries like pigs are not 'dirty' animals; on the contrary they are quite clean, and have the habit of pawing sand against them-selves which is probably a cleaning action. Although the adults are unpredictable, pec-caries have been tamed. One kept as a pet in the United States National Zoological Park in Washington, DC, knew its name and would come when called or when it recog-nised a friend. Apparently it enjoyed having its back scratched with a stick as much as any domestic pig.

class	**Mammalia**	
order	**Artiodactyla**	
family	**Tayassuidae**	
genus	*Tayassu pecari*	*white-lipped peccary*
& species	*T. tajacu*	*collared peccary*

△ *Collared peccary yawns—and shows its tusks.*　▽ *Eating at home: family of collared peccaries.*

△ *Uropygid 'scorpion'* **Thelyphorus caudatus.** ▽ *Amblypygid pedipalp* **Damon variegatus.**

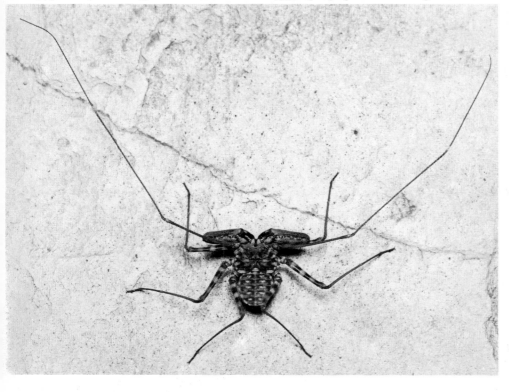

Pedipalpi

The pedipalpi are an artificial assemblage of animals, now regarded as belonging to three separate orders within the Arachnida. The members of two of these groups are both known as 'whip scorpions' but for different reasons: The 'whip' in one group, the Uropygi, is a long thin tactile tail at the end of the abdomen, while the other whip scorpions, the Amblypygi, carry two 'whips' in the form of a pair of very long, flexible legs. All three groups use the first pair of legs as feelers rather than for walking, but in the Amblypygi the length is particularly exaggerated. The members of the third group, the Schizomida, are too small and retiring to be well known. In all three, the body is in two parts, a combined head and thorax, or cephalothorax, and an abdomen of 12 segments. They vary in length from $1-2\frac{3}{4}$ in. The cephalothorax bears the legs and, at the front, a short pair of appendages called chelicerae followed by the well-developed pair which names the group pedipalps.

△ *At death's door? This whip scorpion* **Damon variegatus** *traps and kills insects with its large spiny pedipalps and then dismembers them with its sharp, curved chelicerae. Two pairs of tiny eyes can be seen on top of the cephalothorax.*

Frog-eating tail-rumps . . .

The powerful pedipalps of the Uropygi scorpion-like animals are armed with claws for the capture of cockroaches, grasshoppers and other insects, as well as slugs and worms—or even small frogs and toads in the case of the largest species *Mastigoproctus giganteus,* of Mexico and the southern United States. At the base of each pedipalp is a large semicircular toothed structure used for crushing the prey. There are 8—12 feeble eyes arranged in 3 groups on the cephalothorax, but the first pair of legs are more important as sense organs. In any case, the Uropygi are nocturnal hunters, hiding during the day under logs and stones, or in burrows. *M. giganteus* spends several days digging its burrow with its pedipalps and when it is finished the tunnel may be 4 in.

long. The prey is usually devoured here.

There are about 700 species of Uropygi (literally tail-rumps) living in southern North America and northeastern South America as well as in India, Malaya, eastern Asia and Japan.

. . . split middles . . .

The members of the small group, the Schizomida, are ¼ in. or less long with at most only a knob for a tail. The carapace of the cephalothorax, divided in this order alone into three parts, carries only one pair of eyes. The pedipalps end in spines instead of in claws and they move up and down instead of sideways as in the Uropygi. There are three genera and the group occurs sporadically in tropical regions, appearing sometimes also in botanical gardens such as that at Kew. The Schizomida feed at night, probably on insects and hide by day, though not in any fixed home. When disturbed, they make their escape by a quick backwards leap and can run fast. Little more is known of their habits.

. . . and blunt-rumps

The tail-less Amblypygi, (literally blunt-rumps) have very flattened bodies suitable for getting through narrow cracks and the two halves are joined by a slender stalk. There is one pair of median eyes and three pairs of lateral eyes as in some of the Uropygi. The pedipalps are spined, powerful and sometimes very long, and each ends in a movable hook. There are fewer than 100 species, ¼—1¾ in. long, and they are found in humid tropical and subtropical regions: the southern half of Africa, America, India, Borneo and New Guinea.

Nocturnal like the others, the Amblypygi cling by day to the undersurfaces of rock crevices, logs and stones. Some species, with less need for dampness, have become commensal with man and in some parts of the world few houses are without them. When exposed to light, their first reaction is to freeze, but they will run fast if touched. Usually they walk sideways and then, as well as while at rest, they are continually searching around with the tips of their long

legs. One of the two families consists mostly of small cave-dwellers and these, unlike the others, can run around under the ceilings of caves or even up polished glass. The prey, mostly insects of various kinds, are held in the spiny pedipalps while the chelicerae remove pieces for chewing.

Courtship dances

Courtship and breeding have not been observed in many of the pedipalpi, but at least it is clear that the groups differ. In the Uropygi the courting male holds the long front legs of the female in his pedipalps and chelicerae and walks backwards with his mate following. She responds by lifting her abdomen which the male strokes with his front legs. The sperm is transferred in a spermatophore which is held against the female genital opening for some hours. The pregnant female digs a burrow where she stays several weeks and lays, in one species at least, 20–35 yellowish eggs which are retained in a transparent membrane under her abdomen. The young cut their way out

of this by means of special spines on their legs and cling to the upper side of the mother's abdomen or to the bases of her back legs until they reach the adult form, at the first moult. They then leave the mother whose strength is nearly spent and become adult after three more yearly moults.

In the single member of the Schizomida studied, the mating pair promenade with the female holding the end of the male's abdomen with her chelicerae. He then deposits a spermatophore and cements it to the ground. From the top of this, the female gathers the sperm. Later she builds a little nest with cemented walls under the soil. The Amblypygi court at night, with much tapping of the front legs and threatening with the pedipalps, but no grasping. The male deposits a slender transparent spermatophore on the ground while facing away from the female and then turns towards her and loads it with sperm. As he steps back and quivers, she collects the sperm, leaving the spermatophore for him to eat. She also carries her eggs in a sac under her abdomen.

Exaggerated reputation

With the scorpion-like tails of one group and the exaggerated legginess of the other, whip scorpions are unfailing objects of horror. In fact, they have neither stings nor venomous bites and the Amblypygi, at least, are harmless. Nevertheless, the large *Mastigoproctus giganteus* of southern North America, where it has the local name of 'grampus', is generally feared for its supposed venomous properties. In fact it can inflict a wound with the spines on its pedipalps and, like others of the Uropygi, can discharge a protective cloud into the air from glands near the base of the tail which can be very irritating to the mucous membranes. The secretion of some species smells of formic acid or chlorine, but in *M. giganteus*—called 'vinegarone' or 'vinegaroon' in America—it is acetic acid.

phylum	**Arthropoda**
class	**Arachnida**

Pelican

The pelican is known to many people only from seeing it in zoos or on ornamental lakes where its ungainly appearance often makes it the subject of ridicule. In the wild, however, it is a superb flier and swimmer.

There are eight species, two of which occur in the New World and six in the Old, distributed over the tropical and warm temperate parts of the globe. The species differ only in the smaller details of size, colour and geographical range. Both sexes are alike and all have massive bodies, supported on short legs with strong webbed feet. They have long necks, small heads and a thick, harsh plumage. They are among the largest living birds, from 50—72 in. long. The most conspicuous feature is the enormous beak; the upper part is flattened and the lower part carries a pouch that can be distended to grotesque proportions. It can hold about 17 pints of water and is used, not for storing food, but as a dip net for catching fish.

Apart from the brown pelican, in the majority of the species the adult plumage is mainly white, tinged with pink in the breeding season in some species such as the pink-backed pelican of Africa. The primaries are black or dark. Some species have crests and in some there is yellow, orange or red on the bill, pouch and bare part of the face. The brown pelican, the smallest member of the family, with a wing-span of up to 6½ ft and weighing about 8 lb, has a white head with a yellow tinge. In the breeding season the neck turns a rich brown with a white stripe running down each side. The wings and underparts are dark brown. The larger white species may have a wing-span of 10 ft and weigh 24 lb.

The brown pelican, which is a sea bird that does not venture far from the shore and breeds on small islands, is found along the south Atlantic and Gulf coasts of North America through the West Indies to Venezuela. Along the Pacific it ranges from central California to Chile with one population on the Galapagos Islands. The other New World species is the American white pelican that breeds on inland lakes from western Canada to southern Texas. In the Old World there are pelicans in Africa, southern Asia, including the Philippines, and Australia and in southeast Europe there are isolated colonies of the large silvery white Dalmatian pelican which ranges eastward from there into central Asia, visiting Egypt and northern India in winter. It nested at least as far north as Hungary until the middle of the last century and according to Pliny it nests in the estuaries of the Elbe, Rhine and Scheldt.

▷ Crowning glory! Pelicans often found their colonies in tall trees. The nests, unlined structures of dry twigs, are large and ungainly.
◁ Pink-backed pelican in flight.

Ram Panjabi

Fishing cooperation

Pelicans feed mainly on fish but crustaceans are also taken. The white pelicans fish while floating on the surface or wading about in the shallows. They thrust their heads under the water, using their pouches as dip nets to catch the fish. Occasionally a large flock of birds will cooperate by forming a line across the water and swimming abreast, beating the surface violently with their wings to drive schools of small fish into shallow water where they can easily scoop them up.

Community breeding

Pelicans are very sociable and all the species nest in large colonies sometimes of tens of thousands. Most of the white species breed on isolated islands in large inland lakes usually making their nests on the ground but occasionally they nest in low trees. On the ground the nest is sometimes just a depression scooped out of the earth. The brown pelican which breeds on small islands on the coast, makes a loose nest of sticks in mangrove trees and low shrubs or sometimes on the ground.

In all species the breeding season varies from place to place and from year to year. In some tropical areas they may even breed throughout the year. Chalky white eggs numbering 1−4 are laid which both parents help to incubate for 29−30 days. The babies are born naked and blind but quickly grow a soft white down. Both parents feed the young, at first dribbling regurgitated food out of the ends of their beaks into the chicks' open mouths, but after a few days the chicks are strong enough to stick their heads into their parents' pouches to get the food. Be-

◁ *Spectacular dive − spear-like attack.*
▽ *Head-on collision − clumsy recovery.*
The brown pelican feeds on fish which it sights from the air and then dives onto, rather like a gannet, striking the water with such force that fish as much as 6 ft below the surface may be stunned. The noise of the impact can sometimes be heard ½ mile away. Under the skin of its breast the brown pelican has a layer of air pockets enclosed in membranes which protects it when it hits the water.

fore the chicks are 2 weeks old they leave the nest and form noisy juvenile groups but the parents continue to feed them for some time. The young mature slowly, only acquiring adult plumage after several years. They seldom breed until they are 4 years old. Pelicans are long lived birds. Although the accepted record is 52 years, there are less well authenticated accounts of birds living to a much greater age. The Emperor Maximilian is said to have had a pelican which always accompanied his troops when they were on the march, and that lived for more than 80 years.

Many hazards for the young

Mature pelicans have few natural enemies. Sometimes they may be killed by sea lions in the Pacific or occasionally eaten by sharks but among the young mortality is very high. When the young birds congregate after leaving the nest many fall from trees or get caught in the branches or even trampled on by clumsy adults. When a baby pelican is hurt a larger fledgling is likely to eat it. The adult birds do little to protect their young and sometimes entire nesting colonies are wiped out by predatory animals. It is doubtful if even half the young birds survive. Fishermen have been known to destroy colonies of pelicans to prevent them taking too much fish. At Pelican Island, Florida, in 1911 a plague of mosquitoes caused an entire colony of breeding birds to abandon the rookery, leaving 600 nests containing nestlings. In Peru the guano diggers often damage the nests, knocking young birds out of the way and frightening away the parents, so leaving the chicks an easy prey for predators. Nowadays the pelican colonies are often in danger when marshes are drained or lakes dry up due to large water schemes.

Superb in flight

The pelican has often been described as a clumsy bird, a statement no more justified than it would be to speak of a duck or a swan as clumsy merely because they walk on

▷ *Helping itself. A pelican chick sticks its head into its parent's pouch to get its food.*

James Carr

Series by Jugo H Schroeder

land with a waddle and because the body is heavily built. When a pelican has managed after much effort and flapping to become airborne it is a strong and graceful flier, and it is no less graceful in the water. With legs up, head well back on the shoulders and its large bill resting on the front of the neck it can sail through the air with little effort.

Pelicans seem to possess quite unnecessary powers of flight considering that all their food is taken from the water and everything about them suggests adaptation to an aquatic mode of living. They fly at about 26 mph and there is an authentic record of their having maintained this speed for 8 miles, so it seems they also have the quality of endurance in flight. There is one record of the common pelican having achieved 51 mph. They regularly fly in formation either in line astern or in V-formation, all members of the flight beating their wings in perfect unison. The sight of a flock gliding down like a squadron of flying-boats is spectacular. They also have the vulture's trick of using thermal currents, soaring in spirals to

a great height, even as much as 8 000 ft, where by alternately flapping and gliding they may circle for hours.

Symbol of piety

The principal myth concerning the pelican is that the parent bird, if unable to find food for her brood, pierced her breast with the tip of her bill and fed the youngsters on her own blood, and that is how the bird is figured in the earliest pictures of it. It was because of this belief that the pelican was chosen as an emblem of charity and piety and became a favourite heraldic emblazonment. There is a different version of the story according to Bartholomew. Writing in 1535 he says that the young pelicans smite the parents in the face, whereupon the mother retaliates, hitting them back and killing them. Then, on the third day, the mother smites herself in the side until the blood runs out onto the bodies of her youngsters, bringing them to life again.

These two stories may have arisen because

△ *Fish scoop. A yawning common white pelican shows its enormous pouch for catching fish.*

in feeding its young the parent presses it bill against its neck and breast in order t make the contents of the pouch more readil available to the young, who thrust thei bills into the pouch to take the food. Th red tip on the common pelican's mandibl may also have made the story more plausible

class	**Aves**
order	**Pelecaniformes**
family	**Pelecanidae**
genus & species	*Pelecanus crispus* Dalmatian pelican *P. erythrorhynchos* American white pelican *P. occidentalis* brown pelican *P. onocrotalus* common white pelican *P. rufescens* pink-backed pelican others

eppered moth

The study of the peppered moth has provided us with an example of evolution in progress, the gradual change in form as a result of natural selection. There are three colour forms of the peppered moth. The typical form has white wings 'peppered' with black specks which sometimes form faint black lines. Another form called carbonaria is the black or melanic form, from the black pigment called melanin. The third, an intermediate form, which is black, speckled with white, is called insularia. The females are larger, with a wingspan of about 2¼ in., the males having a wingspan of about 1⅜ in. The males have feathery antennae while the females' are slender and hairlike.

The peppered moth is found throughout Europe and may be identical with a North American moth that is classified as another species Amphidasis cognateria.

Darwin's missing evidence

Darwin's theory of evolution by natural selection lacked final proof: he could give no example of evolution actually taking place. Yet during his lifetime significant changes had taken place in the population of peppered moths in Britain and elsewhere. Before the Industrial Revolution the black or melanic form of the peppered moth, often called simply *carbonaria*, was extremely rare. It occurred as a rare mutant cropping up from time to time like red hair in man. Then, as towns and even countryside became coated with soot from homes and factories, melanic moths became more numerous and in some places the typical peppered moth completely disappeared. The soot not only blanketed the trees, but it also killed the lichens, so the typical form of peppered moth showed up starkly against the dark

▽ *Peppered moths. Typical and melanic forms on soot-covered tree (left) and on lichen (right).*

background of the trees on which it rests during the day and was easily picked off by insect-eating birds. The black variety which had been at a great disadvantage now flourished, because birds failed to see it on a soot-blackened tree. For many years now the peppered moth has been studied by HB Kettlewell and other biologists. They found that black, melanic, peppered moths now predominate in the industrial areas of Britain, and only in rural areas such as the southwest tip of England and the north of Scotland are they still very rare.

The phenomenon of the change from the typical to the black varieties in industrial areas is called industrial melanism and some 10% of the 700 or so larger moths in Britain have changed from a light pattern to dark shades. In all cases they are moths that spend the day resting against a tree trunk or similar background. It must not be thought, however, that a new species has been created, as light and dark peppered moths still interbreed. But it has been shown that an animal's form can change when its environment changes, because under the new conditions the new form is favoured at the expense of the old. Where smokeless zones have been introduced, the situation is being reversed with the typical, light variety once more becoming common.

Night fliers

The peppered moth belongs to the family Geometridae, or geometers as they are popularly known. These are night-flying moths that spend the day resting inconspicuously on tree trunks with the wings flat against the bark. The peppered moth can be found in May and June in woods and parks and its caterpillars feed on trees and bushes such as oak, elm, birch and bramble from July to September. The caterpillars of geometer moths are called 'loopers' because of the way they arch their bodies when walking. The name geometer means ground measurer which is very appropriate. To pupate they burrow into the soil and the adults emerge the following May.

The adults are extremely inconspicuous when they rest on tree trunks, although

many are caught by bats when flying at night. The caterpillars are just as inconspicuous because they resemble twigs. They are green or brown with minute white dots and they rest with their head and body raised at an angle to a twig, hanging on with their hindlegs, or prolegs. Between the two pairs of prolegs are fleshy knobs which assist the camouflage by making it look as if the caterpillar is firmly attached to the twig, by eliminating any shadow under the body.

Proving the case

Since industrial melanism was first demonstrated, careful experiments have been made to show that the change in colour has been due to the effect of predators being able to find typical peppered moths more easily than black ones on a dark background. In other words, to prove that natural selection is taking place it must be shown that one form is better fitted to survive than another.

Dr Kettlewell watched birds catching peppered moths as they rested on trees. He marked large numbers of moths with paint and found that in an unpolluted forest he could recapture twice as many typical as black moths but that the proportion in a woodland close to an industrial city was reversed. This was clear evidence that moths that fitted their background lived longer. In another experiment, dead typical and dead black moths were placed on tree trunks in an industrial area. Birds found 60% more of the typical moths. Furthermore Kettlewell found that when moths were kept overnight in a cage painted with black and white stripes, black moths usually settled on black stripes and typical moths on white stripes, so apparently the moths are actively seeking the right background.

class	**Insecta**
order	**Lepidoptera**
family	**Geometridae**
genus & species	***Biston betularia***

MF Tweedie: NHPA

MF Tweedie: NHPA

Perch

*This fish, which originally gave its name
to the largest order of fishes, the Perci-
formes, was the freshwater perch of Europe.
The name is derived from Greek and
Latin, through the French, and it was
known to the Romans as* **perca**. *There are
many perch-like fishes known today, so the
main attention here will be concentrated
on the European perch. This plump-bodied
fish is dark greenish with a yellowish tinge
on the flanks and dark bars. The undersurface is silvery blue to yellowish, and the
anal and pelvic fins are reddish. The
colour varies, however, from one place to
another, and in some localities the bars
may be missing. The front dorsal fin is
spiny, but both are well developed. There is
a medium sized anal fin, the pelvic fins are
well forward and the tail is almost square-
ended. It usually weighs about 1 lb
although the record is about 10 lb.*

*The perch is found in freshwater in
much of Europe, western Asia and Siberia,
and in slightly brackish waters around the
Baltic. Its counterpart in North America,
east of the Rockies, is the yellow perch,
which is golden with dark bars, a silver
belly and orange anal and pelvic fins. A
near relative in northern Europe, including
the British Isles, is the pope or ruffe, a
somewhat smaller fish with a marbled
pattern and lines of distinct dark spots on
the fins. The walleye or pikeperch of North
America is about the same size as the perch
but has a blotched pattern and prominent
eyes. The pikeperch of Europe and Asia is
about the same size as the walleye. In
North America there are also small darters,
fast-moving, brilliantly coloured fish, only
a few inches long.*

Lying in ambush
These well camouflaged predatory fish lurk
among the stems of water plants, suddenly
dashing out to seize their prey. The mouth
is small but opens into a wide gape. Their
main sense is sight but perch can hear and
smell. There are two nostrils on each side of
the head, one which takes water in and the
other at the rear which lets water out of the
nasal pouch. Inside this pouch is a rosette
of sensitive tissue.

Perch live in shoals in slow-flowing rivers
and lakes. The smaller the fishes, the larger
the shoals, so at 3 years old they swim in
small groups of a half-dozen or less, and
later may even be solitary. In winter they
retire to deeper water, as deep as 30 ft in
lakes, and remain quiescent there. They
can, if necessary, draw upon the oxygen in
the swim bladder for breathing.

Fish food builds bonny perch
The adult perch eat smaller fishes, which
they usually seize from behind with their
sharp teeth, damaging the tail. They then
swallow the fish head-first. The fry, up to
one month old, feed on waterfleas and other
small plankton, after which they eat bottom-

living invertebrates, such as midge and mayfly larvae, freshwater shrimps and occasionally a leech. During July, when the small perch are about 2 months old, there is a tendency towards cannibalism. Perch feeding only on fish grow faster than those forced to eat other food when fish are scarce.

Strings of eggs

Spawning takes place during April and May, the fishes shoaling according to size. The eggs, like those of the American yellow perch, are laid in long strings which become entangled with water plants. In laying them the female glides over the water plants with her fins lowered, shedding the eggs which are then fertilised by one or more males. A large female may lay 200 000 eggs. They hatch in about 18 days, or in only 8–10 days if the weather is warm. The transparent larvae are $\frac{1}{5}$ in. long. On hatching, each larva spirals to the surface to fill its airbladder. After this they hang for a while on water plants, and then float at the surface. Perch mature at 3 years. The maximum recorded life span is $10\frac{1}{2}$ years.

Do fish feel pain?

One of the questions often asked is whether fishes feel pain. The story usually told, to show they do not, is about the angler whose hook fouled the eye of a perch. In freeing the hook the eye was removed and the angler used it as bait, catching the perch it belonged to almost immediately. It is an unpleasant story, yet a point is made. Almost equally unpleasant reading is the fact that since 1825 a dozen or more scientists have tried the experiment of removing the forebrain of fishes, mainly of perch—probably because they were easy to get. The forebrain is the 'thinking' part of the brain. In these experiments it was found that the fishes soon recovered from the operation and, so far as one could see, led quite normal lives. Presumably, therefore, if they feel pain at all, it cannot be to anything like the same degree as human beings.

class	**Pisces**
order	**Perciformes**
family	**Percidae**
genera & species	***Acerina cernua*** *pope* ***Etheostoma nigrum*** *johnny darter* ***Perca fluviatilis*** *European perch* ***P. flavescens*** *yellow perch* ***Stizostedion vitreum*** *walleye* *others*

◁ *A European perch lurks among the water plants waiting for unsuspecting prey. Its deceptively small mouth opens into a wide gape.*

△ *A rather drab relative, the walleye's most notable feature is its prominent eyes, the chief sense organ of perch.*

▷ *Design in eggs. Part of an egg rope of European perch wrapped around a water plant. Developing embryos can be seen inside the translucent eggs.*

John Tashjian

Heather Angel

Père David's deer

This deer has been extinct in the wild for many years and is now known only from the descendents of a herd kept in the Emperor's hunting park near Peking. It was discovered in 1865 by the French missionary and naturalist, Père Armand David. It is quite the strangest of the Asiatic deer; it looks like a donkey with long antlers. The front prong of the antlers is forked but the hind prong is usually straight and slender. Unlike those of other deer, the antlers are sometimes shed twice a year, the summer antlers, measuring 28—35 in. along the curve, being dropped in November and the second, much smaller pair, if they occur, are hard by January and dropped a few weeks later. The females have no antlers. Père David's deer stands about 45 in. at the shoulder and the coat is reddish tawny mixed with grey. The underparts and a ring round the eye are white. There is a mane on the neck and throat and the tail is tufted and longer than that of any other deer. The hoofs are large and spreading.

Original habitat unknown

Even the Chinese did not know where Père David's deer came from originally but it is thought it may have inhabited the swampy plains of northern China until cultivation of the land wiped it out except for some kept by the Emperors in their hunting parks. The species now survives only in herds in Woburn Park, England and various zoos throughout the world.

Unlike most deer it is very fond of water. It swims well and will spend long periods standing in water up to its shoulder. The late Duke of Bedford has recorded in his book *The Years of Transition* that he has seen young stags racing and playing in deep water more in the manner of seals than of deer. Although predominantly a grazing animal, in summer Père David's deer supplements its grass diet with waterplants.

Boxing stags

The rut begins in June when the hinds group together in harems dominated by a stag. The master stag often engages in mock combat and actual fights with rival stags for the possession of the harem. He will use not only his antlers and teeth when fighting but will also rise on his hind legs and box like the red deer. The master stag sires the early calves until driven out by another stag, and this goes on until the rut ends in August. The stags usually keep together, away from the hinds, for about 2 months before and 2 months after the rut, but the sexes are together for the rest of the year. The one or two boldly spotted fawns are born in April and May after a gestation period of 250 days. The life span of the deer is at least 20 years.

Missionary and naturalist

Père David's deer has a quite unusual history. In 1865 Père David looked over the wall of the Chinese Emperor's hunting park near Peking and saw a herd of about 100 strange-looking deer. The Chinese called it *ssu-pu-hsiang* ('the four unlikes') for it was credited with having the antlers of a stag, the neck of a camel, the hoofs of a cow and the tail of a donkey. The Chinese believed the antlers had medicinal properties and they also carved small works of art from them. No stranger, however, was allowed into the park and it was not until the following year that Père David managed, by bribing the Tartar guards, to obtain two skins to send back to Paris. Later, several live individuals were shipped across to Europe to various zoos.

In 1894 a disastrous flood in China breached the wall of the Imperial hunting park and most of the herd of Père David's deer escaped into the surrounding countryside where many were killed and eaten by the starving peasants. Most of the survivors were destroyed in 1900 during the Boxer Rebellion and by 1911 only two remained alive in China and 10 years later both these were dead.

The deer sent to the European zoos did not breed very successfully and in 1900 the 11th Duke of Bedford decided that the only hope of saving the species was to collect all the survivors in one herd in Woburn Park and the famous herd was accordingly started with 18 deer. The park seemed to suit the deer and the herd flourished so by 1939 i numbered about 250. Meanwhile the Duke had been succeeded by his son who decided that with the risk of bombing, food short ages and disease during the war the species might once again face extinction. It seemed far from sensible to keep all the living members of a species in one place. Accordingly he approached the Zoological Society of London in 1944 and with their help day-old calves from the herd at Woburn were sent to Whipsnade Zoo and in time a small herd was established there, and this has continued to increase. Calves from Woburn and Whipsnade were subsequently sent to zoos in almost every part of the world, but perhaps what is of most interest is that in 1956 the Zoological Society of London presented four calves to the Peking Zoo, half a century after the species had been wiped out in China. There are now over 400 of these deer at Woburn and in various zoos.

class	**Mammalia**
order	**Artiodactyla**
family	**Cervidae**
genus & species	***Elaphurus davidianus***

◁ *Père Armand David, who discovered these deer when he looked over the wall of the Chinese Emperor's hunting park in Peking.*
▽ *A mixed society. The male has a fine head of antlers in summer but usually sheds these in November, growing a smaller pair in winter.*
▷ *A stag spends much time wallowing and will use its antlers to hook mud and turves skilfully onto its back, presumably as a pre-rut dressing.*

Peregrine

The peregrine is one of the best known of the falcons and a favourite among falconers. It is a large bird, 15—19 in. long, the female being larger than the male. Its upperparts are slate-blue with darker barrings, its underparts white with black barring. Young peregrines are browner with streaked rather than barred underparts. There are prominent black 'moustachial' stripes on each side of the face. These probably absorb light, so reducing glare from the ground that would prevent the peregrine from seeing its prey clearly.

Peregrines are almost cosmopolitan, living on all continents except Antarctica, and on many oceanic islands. They differ quite considerably throughout their range both in size and colouring, and so are divided into several subspecies. The largest peregrines live in Arctic regions and the smallest in the deserts of North America and Arabia. Peregrines are found over most of Europe and much of Asia and Africa, including Madagascar. They also inhabit most of North America, including the far north, but are absent from the southern parts of the United States and most of Central and South America, except at the southern tip of the continent. Finally they are found in Australia, and the islands to the north.

Alarming decrease

Although found in forests, open plains and moors, peregrines are most numerous in rocky areas of mountains and, in particular, sea cliffs. Each pair defends a territory, the size of which depends on the abundance of food. On cliffs where seabirds nest there may be a pair of peregrines every two miles but elsewhere territories may cover tens of square miles. When not feeding or caring for young, peregrines roost on a favourite perch or circle around their territory. Peregrines breeding in high latitudes migrate in winter, European birds crossing the equator to South Africa, for instance. They follow well-defined routes, usually hugging the coast but sometimes crossing open water. Occasionally the young birds travel with their parents.

In common with many other birds of prey, peregrines are becoming rare. Their decline started with the spread of intensive agriculture and game preserves. During the first half of this century, however, in Britain at least, the peregrine was recovering its numbers, with only a setback in the Second World War when they were killed to protect carrier pigeons being used as messengers. But since about 1955 there has been an alarming decline of peregrines in many parts of the world. This is due to pesticides which become concentrated in the eggs of birds of prey and make them infertile. Seeds treated with tiny amounts of insecticides are eaten by small mammals and birds. As they eat many seeds, larger amounts of insecticides are accumulated. The peregrine eats many small mammals and birds, so concen-

△△ *Blind magnificence: powerful peregrine.*
△ *Falconry was a serious sport in former times, the birds being used to catch game.*

trating the insecticide further. The dose they receive is seldom enough to kill them but when it gets into the eggs it will kill the embryo. In Britain today the population of peregrines is less than half what it was during the immediate postwar years.

Stooping to conquer

Peregrines feed mainly on birds but also on mammals such as young hares, mice and voles and occasionally amphibians and insects. Pigeons are favourite prey, although smaller races take more small birds. Grouse are often caught on moors and seabirds around cliffs. Prey is caught after a swift dive, or stoop, with nearly closed wings and is either killed in the air by being struck with the hind claws or is carried to the ground, and thence to a special feeding place where it is plucked before being eaten. They also sweep birds from their perches but the prey sometimes succeeds in escaping by violent manoeuvres or by hugging the ground. Yet peregrines will also take birds from the ground, as shown by their thefts of poultry. In the Arabian deserts peregrines are flown at bustards which land and fight on the ground. Peregrines are also used to keep other birds away from airfields.

Aerial exchanges

Peregrines mate for life and use the same nest site year after year. Sometimes the nest is a scrape in the ground and at other times the abandoned nest of a raven, herring gull

or buzzard is used. The most popular nest sites are on cliffs and are often inaccessible except to expert climbers. Occasionally peregrines nest on buildings and one pair even used a nestbox put out for it.

At the start of the breeding season the male perches near the nest site and when a female appears he flies out and back, calling to attract her. During courtship the pair dive and swoop or the two tumble through the air together, screaming frequently.

There are usually 3 or 4 eggs in each clutch, although there may be as many as 6. They are laid at 2—3 day intervals and incubation starts before all the eggs are laid so they hatch at intervals after a period of about one month. The female does most of the incubation and is fed by the male who brings food to her on the nest or passes it to her in the air or on a feeding perch. The female is very aggressive, attacking other large birds, men and dogs that come near the nest. When the chicks first hatch the female broods them, then after a fortnight she only covers at night. The male continues to bring food to the female who, in turn, feeds the chicks starting with the oldest. When the chicks are older the male may give food to them directly. These leave the nest when 5—6 weeks old and remain dependent on their parents for another 2 months, sometimes migrating with them.

Incredible speed

Although probably not held in such esteem as the gyrfalcon, the peregrine was a royal bird in mediaeval falconry. Even in strong winds it flies under perfect control and is capable of breathtaking accuracy when stooping, so it is not surprising that it was extremely popular, especially as it is easily tamed. Peregrines can be flown at birds as big as bustards or herons. Arab peregrines may kill seven or eight bustards in a day.

Various attempts have been made at estimating the speed of a peregrine's stoop and recent estimates show that it may be well in excess of 250 mph. This is an incredible speed and poses more problems than merely that of supplying power and streamlining to achieve such a speed. The bones, sinews and muscles must be strong enough to stand the strains imposed, especially during manoeuvring and braking, while the senses must be extremely acute and the reactions quick. One problem that the peregrine has neatly solved is that of breathing air that is rushing past at 200 mph or more. Its nostrils are ridged and within each nostril is a rod with two fins behind it. As air rushes past the nostril the flow is broken up as it swirls past the rod and fins, so little effort is needed to suck it in. Other fast-flying birds of prey have similar structures, but slower species such as vultures and sea eagles lack them.

class	**Aves**
order	**Falconiformes**
family	**Falconidae**
genus & species	***Falco peregrinus***

▷ *The deadly accuracy of a peregrine triumphs again as it towers over a victim, a duck.*

Peripatus

Peripatus is one of the most extraordinary animals living today. A relict from the past, it is a link between the soft-bodied ringed worms, such as the earthworm, and the hard-bodied arthropods, which include insects, spiders and crustaceans.

Its body is rather worm-like, tapering towards the hind end. It is 1 – 3 in. long but can be extended or contracted, and is sinuous in movement. The colour of peripatus is very variable, ranging from dark slate to reddish-brown in the various species, and there is usually a dark stripe down the back. The skin is dry and velvety to the touch and there are 20 or so pairs of short baggy legs each ending in a pair of hooks and ringed like the body. There is a pair of flexible antennae on the head with an eye at the base of each. The eyes are simple although each has a lens. They are directed outwards and upwards and probably do no more than distinguish between light and darkness. The sensory hairs clothing the antennae and most of the body are organs of touch and taste.

Must live in damp places

Peripatus is dependent on moist conditions, being found only in damp forests in South Africa, Australasia and South America. It lives under stones, rotting wood, the bark of fallen trees and similar damp places, being unable to withstand drying. In a dry atmosphere it will lose a third of its weight in less than 4 hours and will dry up twice as fast as an earthworm, and 40 times as fast as a smooth-skinned caterpillar its own size. The cause lies in its breathing system. An insect breathes through branching tubes or tracheae. Because the openings are few there is little loss of water and, moreover, there is an efficient mechanism for closing the openings when necessary. Peripatus has unbranched breathing tubes so it needs far more of them, with an opening to each tube, which means a rapid loss of water from the body when the surroundings are dry. As a result peripatus is found in 'islands', damp localities separated from other colonies by dry country.

Sticky threads for defence

The moment peripatus is disturbed it throws out one or two jets of a milky-white fluid from little nozzles or oral papillae, on the head, one either side of the mouth. On contact with the air the fluid solidifies immediately into sticky beaded threads of slime 3 – 12 in. long. The fluid is in reservoirs, one each side of the head, shaped like the rubber teat of an eye-dropper. Although the threads stick to one's fingers they do not stick to the velvety skin of peripatus itself, but insects and other small animals become entangled in them.

This entangling seems to be accidental because the threads serve more as a defence. Their food is mainly small insects such as termites and they also eat other small animals such as woodlice.

Going for a stroll: a peripatus from New Zealand **Peripatoides novaezealandiae.**

Casual love-making

The mating of peripatus can only be described as casual. The male places capsules containing sperms on the female, apparently at random since he will place them even on her legs. He may place them at times on another male. For a long time it was not known how the sperms reached the ova. Then it was found that white blood corpuscles in the female body migrate to the skin immediately beneath a capsule and break through it by digesting the cells of the skin. At the same time the lower wall of the capsule breaks and the sperms enter the female's blood stream and find their way to an ovary. There in large numbers they force their way through the wall of the ovary. If an immature female receives sperms the young egg cells feed on them and grow for a year before they are ready to be fertilised by a second mating. Except in a few species which lay eggs the embryos develop in the uterus taking in nourishment from the mother through its walls. In one South American species special tissues are formed, making a kind of placenta, to pass food from the mother's body to the growing embryos. Development takes 13 months and as young are born each year there is one month in each year when a female is carrying two sets of embryos, one just beginning to develop, the other nearly ready to be born.

500 million year old fossil of **Xenusion** *(left) looks remarkably like peripatus living today. Diagram (right) of* **Xenusion** *structure.*

Evolutionary bridge

The theory of evolution, in which it is assumed life began in water, requires two main invasions of the land. One, by the vertebrates, meant a change from gill-breathing to lung-breathing and indications of how this may have taken place are seen in the lungfishes (p 1356), the coelacanth (p 481) and the various newts and salamanders. Among the fossils, also, there is an almost complete series showing how this came about. The other invasion is that which brought the invertebrates on land, and the most important change was that from the aquatic ringed worms (see fanworm p 738) and the crustaceans, leading to insects and spiders. If one were asked to draw a hypothetical animal to bridge the gap between the ringed worms and the insects, one could not fail to draw something very like peripatus. Moreover, in its internal structure as well as its outward appearance, this animal looks like the forerunner of both millipedes and centipedes, and they in turn look like forerunners of modern insects. We know from fossils that insects, millipedes and centipedes, in the form we know them today, were already in existence 400 million years ago, so any ancestors linking the two must have been in existence even earlier. It is of interest therefore to find there is a fossil *Xenusion* in the rocks of over 500 million years ago that looks almost the same as peripatus. It is little more than a rusty coloured stain in a piece of limestone rock, yet its shape and the structure of its body and legs can be seen clearly enough to leave little doubt that the peripatus living today and the *Xenusion* of 500 million or more years ago could be closely related. From it or from animals very like *Xenusion* began the line which, through numerous changes, led to the millipedes, centipedes and insects, while another line of descent was continued, almost unchanged, in peripatus. Perhaps the most remarkable thing of all is that peripatus, having become thoroughly land-living, and having acquired a dry skin, should have kept a breathing system tying it so completely to damp areas.

phylum	**Arthropoda**
class	**Onychophora**
genus & species	*Peripatus capensis* *P. moseleyi, others*

DP Wilson

Periwinkle

Periwinkles are just one of the many types of sea snails. The original Anglo-Saxon name was pinewinclan or winewinclan and was applied to the largest of the European species of **Littorina**. *Today periwinkle, or its shortened form winkle, is applied to several related species in other parts of the English-speaking world, notably North America. Zoologically four species of periwinkle are important; they show how the animals of the seashore are arranged in zones, and probably represent marine species that are progressing towards life on land.*

The original or common periwinkle is the largest. Its coiled shell is up to $1\frac{1}{2}$ in. high, and it is the one that, for a long time, has been collected in large quantities for food. Its shell, usually black, sometimes brown or red, is ridged in young, smooth in older individuals. The flat periwinkle with its rounded, flattened shell never reaches more than $\frac{1}{2}$ in. across. Its colour is variable, ranging from bright yellow or olive green, to brown, black or striped. The rough periwinkle has a ribbed shell, with a more pointed apex than the flat periwinkle, is yellow or white, and is $\frac{1}{2}$ in. across and $\frac{5}{8}$ in. high. The small periwinkle, dark reddish brown, is conical, about $\frac{1}{4}$ in. high.

The periwinkle shell has a round mouth which is closed by a dark horny disc, or operculum, permanently attached to the animal's foot. This is popularly called the 'winkle head'. The true head has a broad muzzle and two tapering tentacles with an eye at the base of each. The underside of the foot has a line down the middle and a periwinkle crawls by waves of contraction passing forward along the two halves of the foot alternately. Breathing is by a single feathery gill in the mantle cavity. All periwinkles are vegetarian and, as in other snails, rasp their food to pieces with a horny tongue, or radula.

The rough and common periwinkles are numerous throughout the North Atlantic. The small periwinkle ranges from Scandinavia to the Mediterranean and Black Sea, the flat periwinkle from Iceland to the Mediterranean.

Not knowing which way to turn: these slime tracks left behind on the rocks near high water mark show the aimless meanderings of rough periwinkles in their search for food. Now the tide is out the periwinkles are sheltering in damp rock crevices to avoid the heat of the sun.

Jane Burton: Photo Res

A shore quartet

Four of the periwinkles, although closely related, survive in markedly different situations on the seashore where they may be covered by the tide once every 11–12 hours or exposed to parching sun and wind with no more than an occasional splash of salty spray for many days on end.

The small periwinkle lives in crevices in the rocks up in the splash zone, which is that part of the shore above extreme high tide that is wetted by spray only at the time of high spring tides. It may be completely immersed in water when, especially in winter, storms drive the tides higher than normal. It feeds on lichens, so it is more a land than an aquatic animal, and can survive without water for about 30 days.

The rough periwinkle lives between mid-tide level and the base of the splash zone, uncovered for long periods twice a day. It is, in fact, less tolerant of life in water than exposed to the air, and marked individuals have been found to have survived out of water for long periods. It feeds on seaweeds.

The flat periwinkle lives farther down the shore than the first two, among the larger wracks, on which it feeds, and under which it shelters to keep damp. It also feeds on sponges, especially the purse sponge, but to what extent is not known.

The common periwinkle lives from the level of low water spring tides to high water neap tides, on bare rocks, among seaweeds and stones or on sandy shores. Its tracks over the sand are commonly seen when the tide is out. On hot days, at low tide, however, it tends to get in under seaweed or into damp crevices, or to glue itself to rock surfaces. It gives out a slime from the foot as it withdraws into its shell which glues the edge of the opening to the rock. At the same time it closes itself in with the operculum. Although tight enough to prevent it drying up, its hold on the rock is so loose that a slight gust of wind may blow it off. The common periwinkle feeds on seaweed and especially on fragments broken away that are beginning to decompose.

Different ways of breeding

The sexes are separate, females being slightly smaller than males. In all periwinkles there is a definite mating, with internal fertilisation. The small periwinkle spawns every fortnight from September to April, to coincide with the highest tides and the greatest amount of spray. The larvae spend a long time in the plankton and eventually settle far down the shore and then make their way up to the splash zone 'on foot'. In the rough periwinkle the young develop inside the female and are born as small replicas of the parents. Breeding takes place most of the year. The flat periwinkle lays its eggs in masses of jelly on seaweed, from March to October. There is no swimming larva, the young leaving the jelly as tiny snails. The common periwinkle spawns in spring, the larvae swimming about for 2–3 months before settling on

△ *Cautious movement by a flat periwinkle.*
△▷ *Common periwinkles cluster on a rock.*
△▷▷ *Flat periwinkles on knotted-wrack.*

the shore as tiny winkles of less than pinhead size. The eggs are laid in capsules, 1–3 eggs in a capsule, which float, the larvae coming out of them after 6 days, to swim in the plankton. Each female may lay up to 5 000 eggs in a season.

Poor man's food

Many periwinkles are taken by shore birds, such as gulls and waders, while the tide is out. Oystercatchers, plovers, redshank and such waders feed on them, and when the tide is in bottom-feeding fishes such as plaice take them. They are, however, protected to a large extent from animals that swallow them whole by being able to shut themselves tight in their shells. One periwinkle, for example, was unharmed after being swallowed by a sea-anemone 24 days previously, and they can pass through sea-birds unharmed.

Man has been one of the main predators for centuries. In the 19th century, and in the early part of the 20th century at least, winkles were the 'poor man's food' in England and large quantities were eaten, cooked and extracted with a pin. How far this goes back is hard to say but in the caves in France and Italy, associated with mammoth bones of prehistoric times, necklaces have been found of winkle shells pierced and strung together.

Heather Ange

▽ *Rocky shore zonation: there are 3 basic zones on rocky shores each distinguished by the animals and plants that live in them. This diagram shows the zonation of the four British species of periwinkle and of some seaweeds. The uppermost zone, the splash zone, is only wetted by a few tides a year, or by waves and splash. The small periwinkle lives here. The middle and largest part of the shore, the midlittoral zone, is subdivided into 3 belts. Each belt is inhabited by 1 or 2 species of periwinkle. This zone is exposed to air and covered by sea every day. The sublittoral zone is usually covered by sea. Few periwinkles live here.*

From sea to land

Animals and plants living on the shore tend to be arranged in zones, from high tide mark to low tide mark. In some the zonation tends to be obscured by local conditions, but one that is more clearly marked than most is the zoning of the periwinkles. Another aspect of this is that the arrangement of the four periwinkle species suggests that they are in process of becoming land animals; or, if not that, they suggest how a marine mollusc could become land-living. Three species feed on seaweed, one feeds on lichens. Two breathe by a gill in the mantle cavity which must be bathed with seawater. The other two, the small and the rough periwinkles, have very small gills and the mantle cavity acts as a lung. It only needs the young to develop inside the mother and be born as small but fully formed snails, with no larval period, for a life on land to be within reach, and this has already happened in the small periwinkle.

phylum	**Mollusca**
class	**Gastropoda**
order	**Mesogastropoda**
family	**Littorinidae**
genus & species	***Littorina littoralis*** *flat periwinkle* ***L. littorea*** *common periwinkle* ***L. neritoides*** *small periwinkle* ***L. saxatilis*** *rough periwinkle*

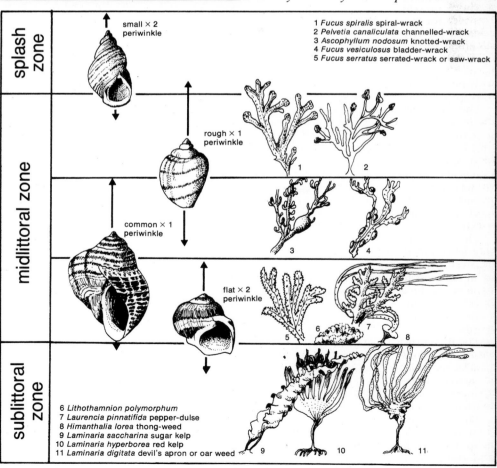

splash zone

small × 2 periwinkle

1 *Fucus spiralis* spiral-wrack
2 *Pelvetia canaliculata* channelled-wrack
3 *Ascophyllum nodosum* knotted-wrack
4 *Fucus vesiculosus* bladder-wrack
5 *Fucus serratus* serrated-wrack or saw-wrack

midlittoral zone

rough × 1 periwinkle

common × 1 periwinkle

flat × 2 periwinkle

sublittoral zone

6 *Lithothamnion polymorphum*
7 *Laurencia pinnatifida* pepper-dulse
8 *Himanthalia lorea* thong-weed
9 *Laminaria saccharina* sugar kelp
10 *Laminaria hyperborea* red kelp
11 *Laminaria digitata* devil's apron or oar weed

Phalanger

*The phalangers make up the largest and most widespread family of Australian marsupials. There are some 46 species in the family Phalangeridae, which includes the cuscuses (p 596), the brushtail opossum (p 295) and the flying phalanger (p 800), as well as the koala (p 1251) which at one time was placed in a family on its own. The word phalanger is Greek and means a web, and it refers to the web of skin joining the small second and third toes. The claws on these two toes are divided and together they form a comb, used for grooming the fur. The name is not derived, as has sometimes been stated, from **phalanges** meaning toes and fingers.*

The kangaroos and wallabies also have the second and third toes on the hindfeet small and joined by a web of skin, but they have only four toes on the hindfoot whereas phalangers have five toes on each foot. In the ringtailed opossums the first two fingers of the forefeet are opposable to the other three and can be used for gripping.

Squirrels outdone

With rare exceptions phalangers live in the tops of the trees, rarely coming to ground. The exceptions include a few, like the rock-haunting ringtailed opossum, and the scaly-tailed possum, which sleeps among rocks but which goes up into the trees at night to feed. Their life in the trees recalls the tree squirrels in other parts of the world, as does the way many of them move through the trees. They go from branch to branch, and from one tree to another, but in doing so they seem to glide rather than bound like the red and grey squirrels of the northern hemisphere. During the day they rest in nests made of leaves and twigs, in hollows in trees.

Phalangers as a group, however, show a greater diversity in shape than squirrels; some have bushy tails, and some have feather-like or pen tails, while others such as the brush-tipped ringtailed opossum have a slight suspicion of a flying membrane. At the other extreme, there are those like the flying phalanger which resemble the flying squirrels very closely. In Africa there are the so-called scaly-tailed flying squirrels. These are not true squirrels but are more nearly related to rats; they have bushy tails that are scaly on the underside near the base of the tail. This scaly part acts as a kind of climbing iron. The scaly-tailed possum has gone one better; its whole tail is scaly and the tip is prehensile.

Tapping for insects

We could go from one to the other of the phalangers and show how between them they seem to have used all the structures found in tree-dwelling animals elsewhere. But perhaps the most remarkable parallelism is seen in the striped possums. Most phalangers are wholly or nearly vegetarian, feeding on fruits and leaves but some also eat some insects. The striped possum, on the other hand, eats a few leaves and fruits but feeds

mainly on insects. It sniffs around and at the same time drums on the bark with its forefeet. Having located an insect grub it tears away the bark and rotten wood with its incisors. If it cannot then reach the grub with its teeth it hooks it out with its very long fourth finger. Except for a few minor details this could be a description of the feeding method of the aye-aye (p 113), a Madagascan lemur.

. . . and his cosy nest of bark strips and leaves.

Forward opening pouch

Female phalangers, except for the koala, have a pouch opening forwards with either 2 or 4 teats in it. Most of them carry one young at a time, rarely 2, but some of the smaller species may bear 5 or 6 young. The breeding and life-history generally seem to be much the same as in kangaroos and wallabies.

Dangers of infancy

Because they are nocturnal, and because they live so much in the tops of trees, most phalangers seem to have few enemies. The present danger to them is the felling of trees to clear the ground. Perhaps one of their main natural hazards is revealed in recent information about the social behaviour of the brushtail opossum. Each female has a territory of $2\frac{3}{4}$ acres, and each male has one of $7\frac{1}{2}$ acres. Young males have difficulty in finding a vacant territory and are harried from pillar to post by the adults in occupation. Where this happens, there is a high infant mortality.

△ *A leaping ringtailed opossum . . .*

Playing possum

There is, and probably will always be, a confusion of names in this family, simply because Captain Cook thought the first phalanger he saw looked so like the North American opossum, as indeed it did. The name of the North American animal was shortened to possum, in about 1613, but zoologists continued to write 'opossum'. When Cook recorded seeing his first Australian animal he wrote 'possum' in his diary, so Australians, the older zoologists among them, continue to call it possum. Although some of the newer generation of Australian zoologists try to use the word 'phalanger' they often, almost unconsciously, lapse into 'possum'.

Perhaps confusion in this matter is appropriate because there is another slight mix-up. The North American opossum is said to feign dead, or play possum, whenever it is alarmed. This has been regarded for a long time as a distinct difference between the two animals. Now we are told by some people who know the American opossum well that they have never seen one play possum. This merely means that they have not seen it, because it does happen, but their experience suggests it is more rare than we used to suppose. Now, in his recent book, *A Continent in Danger*, Vincent Serventy tells of seeing an Australian possum playing possum—the first record we have of this.

class	**Mammalia**
order	**Marsupialia**
family	**Phalangeridae**
genera & species	***Dactylopsila trivirgata*** *striped possum* ***Distoechurus pennatus*** *pentailed phalanger* ***Hemibelideus lemuroides*** *brush-tipped ringtailed opossum* ***Petropseudes dahlii*** *rock-haunting ringtailed opossum* ***Pseudocheirus lanuginosus*** *common ringtailed opossum* ***Wyulda squamicaudata*** *scaly-tailed possum, others*

Phalarope

Phalaropes are small waders with needle shaped bills, and lobes on the toes, like those of coots but not so well developed. The roles of the sexes are reversed and the females are larger and more brightly coloured than the males. In the winter both sexes have drab plumage. The largest of the three species is Wilson's phalarope, about 10 in. long. In its breeding plumage the female is generally slate grey above and white beneath, with red-brown stripes on the back and on the throat. A broad black stripe runs through the eye and down the side of the neck. The male is mainly light brown above and white underneath. The grey phalarope is slightly smaller with a shorter bill. The female, in summer, has distinctive chestnut underparts, white patches over the eyes and a yellow bill. The male is less colourful and in winter both sexes are grey above and white underneath. The grey phalarope is a name used in the British Isles and aptly describes the plumage of those birds that come across the Atlantic in winter. In North America they are called red phalaropes which is appropriate for the birds in their breeding plumage. There are also alternative names for the third species: it is known as the red-necked phalarope in Britain and the northern phalarope in America. It is the smallest phalarope, about 6½ in. long, and has a very fine bill. In the winter it closely resembles the grey phalarope but in summer it is distinguishable by a black bill, slate grey head and upperparts, white throat and underparts and orange patches on the neck.

Phalaropes breed in northern parts of the world, migrating south in winter. The red phalarope breeds farther north than the others, around northern coasts of Alaska, Canada and Asia, as far as Spitzbergen. The distribution of the northern phalarope is similar but more to the south. Wilson's phalarope breeds inland in the central United States and Canada.

▽ Dabbling grey phalaropes resplendent in summer plumage. It is the female, on the right, who 'wears the trousers' for she is the most brightly coloured and aggressive of the pair and establishes the breeding territory.

Deep-sea waders

Although classified as waders, phalaropes do not wade in shallow water but swim, floating very high in the water because air is trapped in their very dense plumage. Wilson's phalarope is an inland bird and sometimes feeds on land but the other two nest near the coast, usually close to ponds or lakes and are virtually seabirds outside the breeding season. They sleep afloat and rarely come to land during the winter. Because they are very light, however, they get blown by gales; they are swept across the Atlantic, for instance, and driven inland to be recorded eagerly by keen birdwatchers.

Stirring for food

Phalaropes feed on land and water, picking up small insects, crustaceans, worms and molluscs in their long bills. A few seeds are also eaten. Wilson's phalarope feeds more on land than the others and may be beneficial, taking large numbers of crane fly larvae and other pests. All three phalaropes have the strange habit of spinning around in the water like a top, at up to 60 revolutions a minute. This may just be due to the birds continually turning to the rear to snap up food. On the other hand they may, by this spinning, set up a small whirlpool that stirs food up from the bottom of shallow water, or disturbs small animals, such as mosquito larvae, which can then be easily seen by their movements. Phalaropes also up-end like ducks.

The red phalarope has the peculiar habit of feeding on whale lice, settling on the backs of surfaced whales like a marine version of the oxpecker. During the Arctic summer they feed on the backs of killer whales and belugas and in their winter feeding grounds in the tropics they settle on sperm whales. They also settle on masses of floating seaweed to reach for small animals living among the fronds.

Topsy-turvy courting

Like button quails and painted snipe, the breeding habits of phalaropes are back to front. The brightly coloured and aggressive females display to each other and establish territories from which they court the attention of the dowdy males. Sometimes several females may pursue one male.

Phalaropes breed in colonies, sometimes quite large, with the nests well spread out. Both sexes build the nest which is a hollow lined with grass. The 4, rarely 3, eggs are incubated by the male alone for about 3 weeks. The female remains near the nest and sometimes helps in tending the chicks.

Chemical breeding control

The differences between male and female lie in both form and behaviour, but in phalaropes these differences are reversed. It is, therefore, of interest to examine the underlying causes of the reversal of sexual characters in phalaropes where courtship and incubation roles have changed without any alteration in the basic roles of the sexes in mating and egglaying. Usually the two are intimately linked; a castrated male chicken changes from the aggressive and amorous cockerel to the timid capon, for hormones secreted by the testes and ovaries control the behaviour associated with breeding. In phalaropes the hormones have been reversed. It is usual for each sex to have both male and female hormones, but for females to have very little male hormone and vice versa. The ovaries of the female phalarope, on the other hand, secrete large amounts of androgen, or male hormone. It is this hormone that is responsible for their bright breeding plumage and their aggressiveness. Male phalaropes incubate the eggs and develop brood patches—the areas of bare skin on the breast which keep the eggs warm. Incubation behaviour and brood patches are controlled by the usually female hormone prolactin of which $3\frac{1}{2}$ times more is found in male than in female phalaropes.

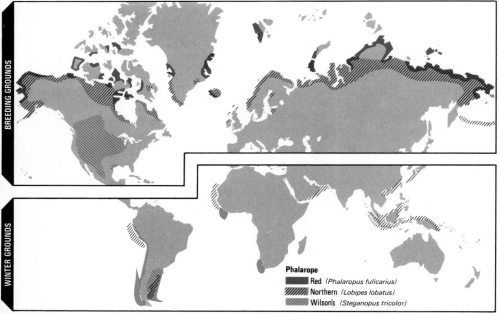

BREEDING GROUNDS

WINTER GROUNDS

Phalarope
Red *(Phalaropus fulicarius)*
Northern *(Lobipes lobatus)*
Wilson's *(Steganopus tricolor)*

▽ *Solitary swimmer, a male red-necked or northern phalarope in his winter plumage.*

▷ *Complete contrast hiding among horsetails, a northern phalarope in summer plumage.*

Eric Hosking

class	**Aves**
order	**Charadriiformes**
family	**Phalaropodidae**
genera & species	*Lobipes lobatus* northern phalarope *Phalaropus fulicarius* *red or grey phalarope* *Steganopus tricolor* *Wilson's phalarope*

Pheasant

The name 'pheasant' comes from the Greek meaning 'the bird from the River Phasis' in the country formerly known as Colchis, to the east of the Black Sea. There are two species of true pheasant but the name has been extended to include monal pheasants, eared pheasants, gallopheasants, longtailed pheasants, ruffed pheasants, peacock pheasants and the argus pheasant. These are all large and beautiful birds with long tails, the males being more showy than the females.

The two species of true pheasant are the green pheasant of Japan and the game pheasant, with many subspecies, from the Caucasus to eastern China and Formosa. The cock game pheasant has a brown plumage marked with buff, black and purple, and a long tail barred with black, but the general effect is of burnished copper. The head and neck are dark green, red wattles surround the eyes and there is a pair of earlike tufts on the head. The hen has a brown, duller plumage. The cock pheasant is up to 35 in. long of which 20 in. is tail, the hen being up to 25 in. of which 10 in. is tail. The game pheasant has been naturalised in many countries and the original subspecies has been crossed especially with the Chinese ringnecked pheasant.

△ Centurion of the game birds, the fabulous golden pheasant living his name to the full.
◁ Haughty handsome arrogance from the most cosmopolitan pheasant, the game pheasant.
▽ 'Observed and sketched from nature by Mr TW Wood', unfortunately this historic drawing of an Argus pheasant displaying is inaccurate but it does show the lines of large eye-spots.

The three species of monals of the Himalayan region are thickset with short, square tails, the males metallic green, blue, purple and coppery red above, velvety black below. The hens are streaked brown. The 10 species of gallopheasants, known as silver pheasants and firebacks, of the Himalayas to Malaysia, have arched tails and velvety wattles on the face. The males are black, blue, purple or white above, black underneath. In the three species of eared pheasants, of China, the sexes are alike. Their plumage is hairlike, the tail is large, there are velvety wattles on the face and long white feathers on the sides of the head. The five species of long-tailed pheasants range from Japan and eastern China to Burma and Thailand. The cock is yellow, coppery red and dark blue marked with black, grey and white. It has red wattles and a long barred tail. The hen is brown marked with black and buff.

The ruffed pheasants include the magnificent golden pheasant and Lady Amherst's pheasant from the mountains of central and western China. The cocks have a crest and a ruff and the plumage is yellow and red in the golden pheasant, green and blue with white in Lady Amherst's pheasant. Peacock pheasants, of the forests from eastern India to Borneo, are small with long tails, grey and brown plumage, marked with metallic green and brown 'eye-spots' and have two spurs on each leg.

1745

A merry band of hen game pheasants tread daintily through the snow. These birds look drab compared with their brilliant male counterpart overleaf.

Fritz Siedel

Unwilling but powerful

Like all pheasants game pheasants are ground birds, feeding and nesting on the ground and roosting in trees. Their wings are short and rounded, and although they do not fly far their flight is strong and fast. If alarmed they run rapidly over the ground, or take off by flying almost straight up, in what looks like a laboured flight. They reach, however, surprisingly high speeds; 60 mph is a figure often mentioned, but whether these are accurate records has yet to be proven. Their legs and toes are strong and spurred, the toes, with strong claws being used in scratching the ground for food: insects, seeds, berries, fallen fruits and leaves, worms, slugs, snails, lizards, even small rodents and young snakes. Roots, bulbs and tubers are also eaten when unearthed.

Driven to distraction

Male pheasants are usually polygamous although there are reports of monogamy when hens are scarce. The cock displays to the hen by blowing up his wattles, puffing up his feathers and parading in front or to the side of her with the wing nearest her drooping and his tail curved towards her. The hen scrapes a shallow depression in the ground and lines it with leaves and grass, usually under coarse grass, bracken or brambles. Some 8–15 olive brown eggs are laid in April and these hatch in 22–27 days, usually being incubated by the hen alone, with the male helping only exceptionally. The young can fly when a fortnight old.

Once called injury feigning, the well-known trick used by a hen pheasant when the nest is in danger is now classed under the general heading of distraction display. When there are chicks in the nest they slip off silently and unobtrusively into the cover of adjacent vegetation and stay still, blending with the background colour. The hen, at the same time—and she will do this also while the eggs are unhatched—runs from the nest, trailing a wing as if injured. A ground predator, such as a fox, follows what looks like a disabled parent who leads him on for up to 100 yd before taking wing and, flying in a wide curve, returning to a point near the nest and disappearing into cover until all is safe.

Sleepyhead beware

In their native home pheasants are killed by the usual birds and beasts of prey and their eggs and chicks taken. When naturalised in foreign countries they are often protected by keepers who kill off any bird or beast that might attack the pheasants or their nests. Domestic cats will wait at dawn for pheasants to come down from their roosts and this is probably the pattern of hunting used by natural ground predators in the pheasants' native home.

An eye for the ladies

The argus pheasant lives deep in the jungles of Malaya, Sumatra and Borneo. The male is 6 ft long, including a long tail and he makes a clearing in the forest on which to display to the female. The secondary flight feathers of his wings are enormously long and each is decorated with a line of large eye-spots—Argus in Greek mythology was a monster with 100 eyes. The argus pheasant is mainly brown and grey but when the male displays he raises the wing feathers to form a huge fan. The bird was made famous by Darwin's account of it in his *Descent of Man*, published in 1871, with an artist's drawing of the pheasant in display. This picture was copied many times in books of the period but was found to be incorrect in detail when David Seth-Smith, then Curator of Birds at the London Zoo, photographed the display in the mid-1920's. The main point is, however, that Seth-Smith's photographs show the pheasant peeping through a space at the angle of the wing for all the world as though he is watching to see what effect his fine feathers are having on the hen.

class	**Aves**
order	**Galliformes**
family	**Phasianidae**
genera & species	***Argusianus argus*** *argus pheasant* ***Chrysolophus amherstiae*** *Lady Amherst's pheasant* ***C. pictus*** *golden pheasant* ***Crossoptilon mantchuricum*** *brown eared pheasant* ***Lophura spp.*** *firebacks and silver pheasants* ***Phasianus colchicus*** *game pheasant* ***Syrmaticus soemmerringi*** *copper longtailed pheasant* ***S. reevesi*** *Reeves longtailed pheasant* *others*

Phoronid

With their crown of tentacles phoronids are tube-dwelling marine worms which are sometimes taken for one of the many annelid worms because of their similar habits. However, 15 or so species of **Phoronis** *and* **Phoronopsis** *make up a phylum of their own, the Phoronida. The crown of tentacles, covered with cilia and used for collecting food, is known as a lophophore. It is also found in moss animals and lampshells and the three groups are thought to be related, though superficially unlike. The tentacles of phoronids number from 18 to well over 500 according to species and age. They are arranged in a single row along each of two basal ridges that curve together to form a horseshoe or crescent, with the mouth between. Sometimes the two ends of the crescent are spirally rolled increasing the length of the ridge and so the number of tentacles. Below the crown, and marked off from it by a slight groove or by a collar, is the body which is slender and uniformly cylindrical except where it widens at the hindend into a bulb. Though faintly ringed, it is not segmented as in earthworms and other annelids, nor does it bear any appendages. It is muscular and contains a long U-shaped digestive tract lying within a space — the coelom. The digestive tract runs from the mouth down to the expanded far end of the body and back again to an anus just outside the crown of tentacles. This is clearly a good arrangement for a tube-dwelling animal. There is a system of blood vessels containing blood cells that are red, like ours, with haemoglobin. Most species are small, about ¼ in., but one,* **Phoronopsis californica**, *found on mudflats on the North American west coast, can exceed 12 in. This species has an orange body and bright red tentacles.*

Tube dwellers

Phoronids live in shallow waters, down to 180 ft, in tropical and temperate seas. They spend all their time in tubes which they secrete around themselves. These tubes may be calcareous or they may be horny and coated with pieces of stone and shell. The phoronids may occur singly, their lower ends embedded in sand or mud, or they may form tangled masses on rocks and wooden piles. Other species burrow into limestone or the shells of molluscs including the British species *Phoronis hippocrepia*. *Phoronis australis*, of Australia, India and Japan, is unusual; it entwines its delicate transparent tubes within the material of the tube of another animal, the tube-living sea anemone *Cerianthus*. Often there are 20 or 30 associated with each anemone. This phoronid does little more than push the front end of its body out of the tube and spread its tentacles, then suddenly withdraw it when disturbed. The individual tentacles show little independent movement and small particles of food are caught by water currents set up by the beating of cilia, mostly on the inner side of each tentacle. Water flows in between the two rows of tentacles and out between the bases of the tentacles while food particles are caught in mucus and wafted by the cilia towards the mouth. Inedible particles are rejected as they get near the mouth or are driven to the tentacle tips, against the general current, there to be rejected, the tentacles bending outward in response to their presence.

Unusual powers of regrowth

Though phoronids normally withdraw promptly when disturbed, the crowns of tentacles are nevertheless sometimes bitten off by predators. However, they can be regrown and it has also been noticed that phoronids kept in aquaria often cast them off by muscular action and regenerate new ones. In one very small species the cast crowns grow new bodies but this is unusual. One species *P. hippocrepia* degenerates in unfavourable weather, in winter off Naples, in summer off Japan, leaving only a few fragments of itself in the tube. When conditions become favourable once more new individuals are formed from these fragments. In a group capable of this amount of regeneration, we can expect asexual reproduction to occur, but this has only been described for one species *Phoronis ovalis* where the animal splits across the middle of the body, to form two individuals, or else gives off buds. In either case, the hind part of the body grows a new crown of tentacles which projects from a new length of tube made at right angles to the old one.

An exquisite actinotrocha larva of **Phoronis** *seen from the side. It is found in the summer plankton feeding on microscopic organisms which are collected by the cilia on the hollow tentacles (× 70).*

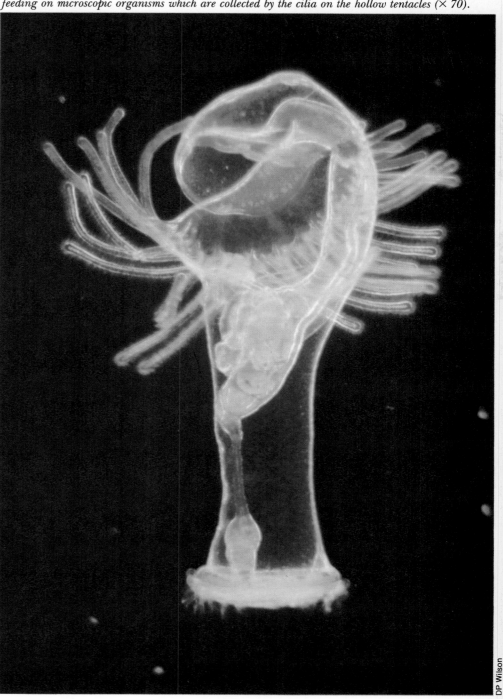

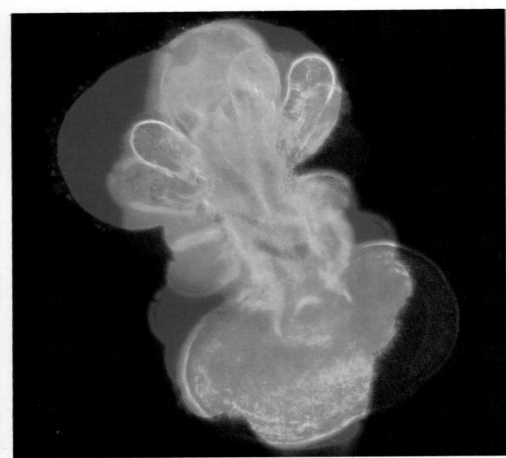

*A young actinotrocha larva or **Phoronis** seen from below (about × 300).*

*▽ **P. psammophila**. Once out of its sandy tube its feeding tentacles can be seen (× 90).*

DP Wilson

AJ Southward

Different ways with eggs

In the northern hemisphere, phoronids breed mostly in spring and summer. In some species there are separate males and females, but the majority of phoronids are hermaphrodite. When the sex cells are ripe they are released into the body cavity and spawned through the pair of excretory organs. In some species fertilisation occurs while the sex cells are still inside this cavity, and in others only after they have been shed into the water. The eggs may be shed directly into the sea or they may be brooded for a while in the shelter of the tentacular crown. One species is exceptional in plastering its eggs to the inside of its tube or to a nearby rock with a sticky secretion. Eventually the eggs hatch to give rise to planktonic larvae that swim freely by means of cilia, some of which are arranged in a ring at the hindend — the main propulsive organ. Gradually the larvae put out about 6—24 hollow ciliated tentacles. When fully developed these larvae are called 'actinotrochs' and are commonly found in the summer plankton. They may be up to $\frac{1}{8}$ in. and have a large hood bent forward over the mouth. For several weeks, the larvae swim about feeding on microscopic organisms gathered by their cilia, but eventually they become sluggish and sink to the bottom. Then in only 15—30 minutes they undergo a rapid metamorphosis involving convulsive contractions of the body and the eversion of a large pouch to the exterior. This pouch enlarges and becomes the body wall of the trunk. Carried out with it is the middle part of the digestive tract which is thus thrown into the characteristic hairpin loop. The hood over the mouth shrinks and is cast off and eaten along with the larval tentacles, while new tentacles arise from buds. After these drastic changes, the young worm starts to secrete its tube.

Two names, one animal

Phoronids were first known from their larvae, found by Johannes Müller in 1845 in large numbers at the surface of the sea near Heligoland. Thinking they were adult animals, Müller named them *Actinotrocha branchiata*. It was not until 1856 that Dr Strethill Wright of Edinburgh found the adults. He had been sent a stone from Ilfracombe in Devon with a coral growing on it. On it were little worms which Wright named *Phoronis*, from an epithet applied to Io of Greek mythology. He gave them the specific name of *hippocrepia* for the horseshoe shape of their crowns. Wright, however, did not realise he had found the adults of the actinotroch larvae nor was this known until several years later, when the actual metamorphosis was seen. Now according to the International Rules of Zoological Nomenclature when an animal is given two names the earlier, in this case *Actinotrocha*, must be used. *Phoronis* has, however, remained the accepted name in spite of the efforts of some scientists to change it.

phylum	**Phoronida**
genera	*Phoronis*
	Phoronopsis

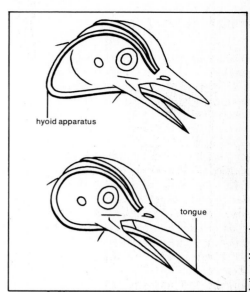

Anthony Maynard

*Male white-bellied piculet **Picumnus spilogaster**. It ranges from Venezuela, Guyana, and Surinam, to Brazil. As shown in the diagram the flexible tongue which 'wipes up' insects is part of an apparatus of bones and elastic tissue, known as the hyoid, and when this apparatus is slipped round the head the tongue is protruded.*

Piculet

Piculets are small woodpeckers, between 3 and 5 in. long. In appearance and habits they are more like nuthatches than typical woodpeckers. An important difference is that the tail feathers are not stiff and pointed, so the tail does not have the tattered appearance seen in the true woodpeckers. One toe, however, is turned back in true woodpecker fashion.

There are eight species of piculet. Two live in southeast Asia, one in western and central Africa and the rest in tropical Central and South America and the West Indies. They are generally grey or green above with spotted or streaked underparts. The olivaceous piculet, the only species on the American mainland north of Panama, has olive-green upperparts, throat and upper breast.

The tail is black with a broad stripe of yellow and the belly is yellowish. The top of the head is black with white dots and fine orange streaks in the male only. The Antillean piculet, of Hispaniola and Gonave Island, has greenish upperparts with yellowish white underparts streaked with black. Both sexes have a yellow crown, but the male's has a red centre. The rufous piculet of Malaya is olive green above, rufous below. The forehead of the male is yellow, whereas the female has a rufous forehead.

Acrobatics in the canopy

Piculets hunt in tropical forests by hanging among the fine twigs in the tree canopy, agilely working their way through them and hanging at all angles, like tits. They go about in pairs or small family groups. Sometimes they work on trunks in the manner of nuthatches, but as they lack the stiff tail feathers of woodpeckers they do not press their tails against the trunk as a support while they are hammering.

Hammer-blows for insects

The bill of a piculet is the same shape as that of a true woodpecker but is comparatively smaller and not so sharp. Nevertheless, piculets feed by hammering at wood or searching bark for insects. They cannot drill holes except in the softest wood but they hammer more vigorously than tits or nuthatches, which also search for insects hidden in wood. The olivaceous piculet is very fond of ants and hammers to bring them out. Larvae and pupae are eaten as they are exposed by the damage done by the bill.

Nest drill

Despite their comparatively weak bills, piculets carve out their own nest chambers. The rufous piculet is often found in bamboo jungles and makes its nest chamber simply by boring a hole in a bamboo stem. The olivaceous piculet drills out its chamber, choosing trees that have decayed to almost balsa-wood softness. The nest is built near the ground, not more than about 5 ft up, and is not lined. Both sexes take part in drilling the nest, sometimes working to-

gether, exchanging trilling calls as they work. One pair kept under observation took about a week to complete the nest. Afterwards they both slept in the nest at night and by day they took turns to incubate the 2 glossy white eggs. The chicks were naked and blind when they hatched. Their eyes opened at 8 days and the feathers sprouted at 16 days. The parents fed them, mainly on the larvae and pupae of ants.

The chicks leave the nest when 24–25 days old but return to the parents at night for another 3 months. Olivaceous piculets often have to make new nests or sleeping holes because the rotten trees they choose are liable to fall down.

Long tongues

One of the distinguishing features of the woodpeckers, including the piculets, wrynecks and flickers (p 783), is their extraordinarily long tongues, which are used to 'wipe up' or spear insects, often from narrow crevices or holes. The tongue is supported on a long, narrow bone which divides into two horns. This structure is common to all birds, but in the woodpecker family the horns are extremely long. They pass from the base of the lower mandible under the skull, round the back and over the top. In the piculets, and some of the flickers and woodpeckers, the horns stop at the base of the upper mandible, but in other flickers and the wrynecks and woodpeckers they continue into one side of the upper mandible or curl under the right eye. A muscle runs from near the tip of the lower mandible and along the length of the horns. When it contracts the horns are pulled forward and pressed against the skull, so forcing the tongue out. The tongues of piculets are long, but the record is held by the green woodpecker with its 6in. tongue.

class	**Aves**
order	**Piciformes**
family	**Picidae**
genera & species	***Picumnus olivaceus*** olivaceous piculet ***Sasia abnomis*** rufous piculet

Piddock

Piddocks are marine bivalve molluscs that bore into stone, wood, peat and sand with a remarkable rotary action. Their shell is broader at one end than the other. The outer surface at the broad end is toothed like a file and is used for rasping. When in the burrow a pair of long siphons reach up towards its mouth, and if disturbed the piddock discharges a jet of water through these. The siphons are united right up to the tip and are partly covered with the horny material that covers the shell. One siphon draws in a current of water, bringing oxygen and food particles, while the other gives out a waste-carrying current.

Besides having a file-like end the shell must be made to scrape. This is made possible by an unusual arrangement in the hinge. In most piddocks the ligament found in other bivalves has been lost and the hinge teeth reduced to a double ball joint. The latter allows the two valves of the shell to rock on each other in a see-saw movement, by alternate contractions of the two adductor muscles, one in front of and one behind the hinge. In other bivalves these muscles run from valve to valve and contract in unison to close the shell. In the piddock, the adductor muscle nearest the front of the animal is the larger of the two and part of it is spread outside the shell and joins the valves above the hinge. In some piddocks, this exposed muscle is protected by one or more extra plates of shell. At the front of the shell where the foot emerges there is, in most species, a permanent gape. Apart from this region, the flaps of mantle tissue that lay down and line the shell are joined up, so the gills are not visible between the edges of the shell. This almost complete enclosure of the gills within the mantle cavity is common in boring and burrowing bivalves.

The name 'piddock' came into use in the early 18th century but it is not widely used outside Britain. These molluscs are therefore known, in North America for example, as rock-borers, rock-boring clams or merely as pholas, from the scientific name of the best known of them. Wherever they occur they are very similar to the European species. The common piddock, the largest, up to 6 in. long, ranges from southern Britain to Morocco, the Mediterranean and Black Seas. The little piddock, $2\frac{1}{2}$ in. long, makes horizontal rather than vertical burrows. The oval piddock, $3\frac{1}{2}$ in. long, is found all round the northern coasts of Europe as well as the British Isles. The paper piddock is peculiar in that when it has finished burrowing, and is at most $1\frac{1}{2}$ in. long, the gape in the shell through which the foot is pushed out becomes closed off by extensions of the shell, which also becomes trumpet-shaped at the base of the siphons.

△ A boring life. The common piddock, as do all piddocks, bores into rock essentially for protection. The shell is cut away at the front where there is a perpetual gape through which the rounded foot projects. This acts as a sucker, gripping the head of the boring and so anchoring the piddock firmly to the rock.

▷ When the piddock has successfully bored into rock its siphons protrude at the tunnel's entrance. In this photo the outer part of the hole has been cracked away to expose fully the long and united siphons. Their position is shown below in an American rock-borer **Pholadidea loscombiana.**

△ *Close-up on piddock holes. The piddock usually continues boring throughout its life. Although safe from enemies in this solitary confinement, there is no escape: as it bores deeper into the rock it grows and makes a wider tunnel so escape back along the narrower, older tunnel is impossible.*

▽ *The shell of the common piddock is elongate, white and rather delicate with up to 50 longitudinal rows of spines where ribs and concentric ridges cross. The extra shell plates which protect the shell-closing adductor muscles are prominent between the valves on the upper surface of the two main shells.*

Rotary borers

Except in the paper piddock, boring generally continues throughout the piddock's life and, as the animal grows, the inner end of the tunnel becomes wider than the older part bored when the piddock was younger. Needless to say, the piddock cannot leave its burrow. Except in the white piddock, which is more suited to boring in softer materials, the foot ends in a broad sucking disc and, as the valves open, the shell is rotated by the foot muscles alternately one way and the other to make a circular hole.

Mechanism of feeding

Piddocks feed in the same way as other bivalves. Fine particles are sucked in through one siphon and strained from the water by the gills, caught in mucus and passed to the mouth. The water currents and the highly organized streaming of the food particles over the gills, over the sorting areas of the lips (labial palps) to the mouth and even inside the stomach, are all the work of the cilia. Sand and other rejected particles are wafted by cilia into the current in the outgoing siphon where they are joined by faeces and materials from the excretory organs. This current also carries out the sex cells in the breeding season. Little more is known of the breeding habits.

Wasted sparks

Although the production of light is not unusual in the animal kingdom, it is hardly what one would expect of a piddock hidden away in a rock. Yet the common piddock has three pairs of powerful light organs that secrete a luminous slime. Inside the outgoing siphon, and for about two thirds of its length, are two long, thin glandular strips, and there are two triangular glandular patches on the outer sides of the muscles that retract the siphons. The third pair are again long and narrow and run around the inner edge of the mantle so as to partly surround the foot opening. The slime is on occasion shot out of the siphon, its release being under nervous control, but its function is not known, even if something is known of its chemistry. Réamur was the first to discover, in 1793, that the slime could be dried and still be made to give out its greenish blue light on the addition of water. Dried slime can be preserved for a year or more. Dubois studied the matter further in 1897 and discovered that the light is the result of a reaction involving two substances which he called luciferin and luciferase. The luciferin is secreted in granules which luminesce as they dissolve, a reaction which requires oxygen and the presence of the enzyme luciferase, though certain oxygen-supplying chemicals such as potassium permanganate or hydrogen peroxide can be substituted for the latter.

phylum	**Mollusca**
class	**Bivalvia**
order	**Eulamellibranchia**
family	**Pholadidae**
genera & species	***Pholas dactylus*** *common piddock* ***Pholadidea loscombiana*** *paper piddock, others*

Pig

Domesticated pigs, or hogs, are derived from two wild species, the European wild boar and the Chinese wild pig. The Indian or crested wild boar may have contributed, but this is doubtful. It is not certain whether these three animals represent three different species or whether they are one species ranging across Europe and Asia as far as the East Indian islands, as well as North Africa. The tendency today is to accept the latter idea. One reason for the uncertainty is that the wild pigs in question show a great deal of variety. One that probably must be separated from the rest is the pygmy hog of Nepal which is only 1 ft high at the shoulder.

The Eurasian wild boar—the Chinese and Indian being grouped with it— usually grows to 4 ft head and body length, sometimes up to 6 ft. Its tail may be up to a foot long, and height at the shoulder up to 3 ft. The boar's weight may be up to 420 lb, the sow's up to 330 lb. Its tusks may be a foot in total length, including the continually growing root. The Eurasian wild boar is pale grey to brown or black in colour, the body hairs being sparse bristles with some finer hairs; the tail has only short hairs. Some individuals have longer hairs on the cheeks or a slight mane, or both.

▷ *Food for pigs. In a forest clearing in Germany 250 wild pigs gather for their evening meal, put out for them by the local inhabitants.*
▽ *Bliss! A wild boar wallows in muddy water.*

The family party

The social unit of the pig is usually the family party but in the autumn family groups come together to form bands of up to 50 females and youngsters, the old males mainly remaining solitary. Pigs live mainly in open woodlands, especially where there are mud wallows in which they will spend many hours at a time if undisturbed. They also make crude shelters by cutting long grass then crawling under it to lift it so that it becomes entangled with the tall herbage around to form canopies. Quick footed and good swimmers, pigs normally avoid combat but will act vigorously when provoked, slashing with their tusks.

Nocturnal rootings

Wild pigs may travel far in a night rooting for anything edible. They will eat acorns and beechmast, roots of various kinds, fallen fruits, even the roots of ferns which few other animals eat. They have a natural tendency to dig for the potato-shaped fungi known as truffles. They will also eat insects, lizards, eggs, leverets, fawns, mice, voles, carrion, and any birds they can seize, in fact a very mixed diet. If allowed, they play havoc among cereal crops and root crops such as beet or turnip, and among potatoes. For this reason they have been hunted for centuries, although they have also been hunted for their flesh and for the sport they give.

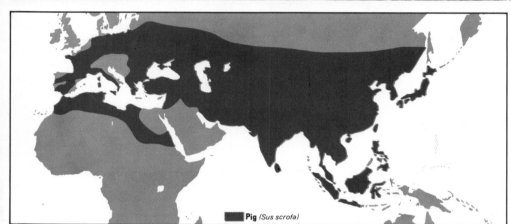

Pig (Sus scrofa)

△ *Two inhabitants of the forest, a boar and a fox, seek food and water on a winter evening.*
▽ *Two wild boar emerge into a forest clearing. The snow makes it harder for them to get food.*

△ *The dark form of a wild boar on its way through a white forest.* △ *A wild boar kicks up its heels and runs. They are not often aggressive.*

Striped young

The sow is in season every 3 weeks and produces litters of 3–12 after a gestation of 112–115 days. She has 8–14 teats and as each piglet takes a teat at feeding time the weaklings in a large litter will die. They suckle for about 12 weeks before being completely weaned onto food which they find while rooting around, never very far from the protection of their mother. The boar takes no part in caring for the young. These young are striped, like other wild pigs. They are sexually mature at 18 months, and reach full size at 5–6 years of age. The pig has a life-span of up to 27 years.

Early domestication

Wild pigs cannot be readily herded but they take well to life in stys or in houses, so we can be fairly sure that their domestication must have come about when men ceased to be hunters and settled down to agriculture. Another clue is in the taboo on eating pig flesh, which seems to have originated in the nomads' contempt for the agrarian communities, expressed in a supposed disgust at the pigs they kept. This was probably reinforced by the disease trichinosis, that could be contracted from eating insufficiently cooked pork. The earliest domestication date is uncertain but it is unlikely to have been before the Neolithic period, with its agricultural revolution.

The European wild boar is larger than the Chinese pig. They represent extremes of a range in size and the evidence is that pigs were domesticated from local races, so giving domestic pigs of various sizes. There is evidence also that in prehistoric times there was importation of breeds from one part of Eurasia to another as well as some selective breeding. So there was a mixture before modern selective breeding began, making it difficult to trace the lineage of present-day domestic pigs.

The pig has been bred almost solely for its flesh and for its fat. Its bristles have been used to some extent for making brushes and the hide for making sandals and other fancy leather goods. Even the bones may be ground up for bone meal fertilizer. Nevertheless, the domestic pig as a living animal has been put to a variety of uses. It has been used for sacrifices; and for a curious custom among the armies of the Roman period, of swearing an oath on a pig or a piglet. Pigs have at various times been used for pulling carts. They have also been trained to detect truffles, which the owner then dug up. In Ancient Egypt pigs were used for treading in corn, their sharp hoofs making holes of the correct depth for the seed to germinate. Most surprising of all, they were trained in mediaeval England as pointers and retrievers for illicit hunting, in the New Forest, for example. There commoners were forbidden to keep any but the smallest dogs, capable of passing through King Rufus' Stirrup, an iron stirrup 10½ in. high by 7½ in. across. In southern India, where there lives a primitive tribe whose buffaloes wander into the marshes, an old woman was seen to speak to a pig which 'at once trotted into the marsh, rounded up the buffaloes and herded them to her, like a well-trained collie'.

class	**Mammalia**
order	**Artiodactyla**
family	**Suidae**
genus & species	***Sus cristatus*** *Indian wild boar*
	S. salvanius *pygmy hog*
	S. scrofa *European wild boar*
	S. vittatus *Chinese pig*

▽ *The good life? A fat, pink, domesticated sow feeds her hungry offspring.*

Pigtailed monkey

Pigtails are big monkeys, the largest of
the macaques (p 1365), but distinctive
enough, together with their close relatives,
the longtailed monkeys, to be treated
separately. The male weighs 20—30 lb,
the female 15—20 lb. The coat is buff or
brown, and the distinguishing feature of
the pigtail is the whirl or parting in the
middle of the crown of the head from which
radiates a 'cap' of short, dark brown or
blackish hairs. The hair around the cheeks
is light-coloured and outwardly directed.
The face has a long light brown muzzle
and lighter eyelids. The short thinly-haired
tail, only $\frac{1}{3}$ the length of the body, is
carried arched over the back with the tip
resting lightly on the rump.

The liontail is smaller, the males weighing only 15 lb, and in it the distinguishing
features of the pigtail are almost cari-
catured. Its fur is black and there is the
same short-haired cap on the crown as in
the pigtail. The cheek-hairs form a long
grey ruff, and the whitish eyelids are conspicuous against the black face. The tail,
though longer, about half the body length,
is similar to that of the pigtail, and may
be carried arched forwards or backwards.
It, too, is short-haired, but as if to em-
phasise the thinness of the tail hair there
is a tuft at the end. 'Lion-headed' would
be as apt a description for this monkey.

Pigtails live in Burma and Vietnam
south to Malaya, Sumatra and Borneo.
They have been introduced into the
Andaman Islands. Liontails are restricted to a small area in the Western
Ghats of southwest India, at heights of
2 500—4 300 ft, where the trees grow to
70 ft or more. They are rare and still
decreasing, being found recently in only
four hill-ranges: the Nilgiris, Anaimalis,
Cardamoms and around Lake Periyar.

▷ Liontailed monkey

Family portrait. Pigtailed monkeys are almost human at times, and like humans, have a great need for social contact, even if it is only visual. In the wild they live in large troops.

Zoological Society, London

Monkey plant collectors

Pigtails make good laboratory animals, especially for psychological experiments. They are much easier to handle than the more nervous and rather vicious rhesus or crabeaters; they are easy to train and co-operate willingly with the experimenter, thus avoiding the stress that so often mars experiments on the mental abilities of monkeys. Experimenters have been struck by the differences between pigtails and other macaques: they stand boldly, unmoved, with their hands turned outwards, quite undisturbed provided they have the company of others of their kind. There is none of the bar-shaking or threatening of other monkeys, their size is the only drawback.

In Malaya, pigtails are caught when young and kept with human families, and trained to collect coconuts. They readily obey words of command, are easily tamed, and safe to handle. At a word of command they will climb palms, twist off the coconuts and drop them to the ground. EJH Corner reports that a pet pigtail that he had could discriminate between the Malay words *mari* (come), *lari* (run) and *chari* (search for), and react accordingly. Undoubtedly, as he points out, the accompanying gestures helped the monkey to interpret correctly.

When shown its image in a mirror, a pigtail will approach cautiously and touch it, then withdraw, making its characteristic pouting face. This pout, made with lips protruded and pressed together, is a facial expression made only by pigtails and liontails among monkeys: it implies a tendency to flee with conflicting social attraction, and is the equivalent of the lip-smacking gesture of other macaques. Then the pigtail approaches again, puts its arm behind the mirror, and gropes about for the other monkey, his eyes all the while fixed on the image. There is no idea in its mind that the 'other monkey' is itself.

The comparative docility and unflappability of the pigtail have enabled us to see many almost human traits in its behaviour. Its need of social contact is one: a pigtail that has been isolated from others will usually not feed—but can often be persuaded to do so if fed by hand, implying that a human companion is the next best thing to another pigtail. It is often enough for a pigtail just to have sight of another. This counts as 'contact', which is often all that can be permitted in the laboratory, as a big male may bully a smaller animal. When undergoing psychological tests, pigtails are more patient and persevering than most other monkeys: rhesus monkeys are more impatient, baboons more destructive. Pigtails show distinct preferences to use one or the other hand for grasping, though some are ambidextrous; they are also right- or left-footed, and even right- or left-eyed—just like man.

Whooping troops

Pigtails and liontails both live in tropical rain-forest, spending more time in the trees than most macaques. They live in large troops: Sugiyama's two liontail troops had 16 and 22 members respectively, while in Malaya Irwin Bernstein found two pigtail troops of 30 and 47 respectively. The troops have overlapping home ranges, about $\frac{1}{4}$ ml in diameter. Each troop contains two or more fully adult males one of which is dominant and leads the troop while another, or a young male, brings up the rear. Some solitary males live in and around the troop areas. When two troops approach one another to feed on fruit trees that are in the overlap area of their home ranges, the adult males whoop loudly at each other. The smaller troop usually moves away after a few minutes—fighting has never been seen between troops. A large troop may break into two for some hours before rejoining.

Dissecting nuts

Like other macaques, pigtails and liontails have a varied diet. They eat mainly fruit and leaves, but also nuts, flowers, buds, pith and grubs. They pick nuts apart, meticulously peeling them with both teeth and fingers, before eating them.

Lonely breeding

There is no distinct breeding season. A mating pair is often found far from its troop. A single young is born after 170 days; it has brown hair and a flesh-coloured skin. In one month the skin becomes pale brown and then gradually turns black. The hair of the liontail turns completely black except for the face ruff. Only the 'cap' on the head turns blackish in the pigtail. Baby pigtails are weaned at 8 months. A pigtail lived for $26\frac{1}{2}$ years in Milwaukee zoo.

Survival by cross-breeding

Tigers and leopards may kill pigtails and liontails but man is their only serious predator. Liontails have been heavily overhunted, and it may be that only 1 000, or even less, still exist. Pigtails are more resilient, but even then they have suffered at man's hand. In heavily cultivated areas the little crab-eating macaque (see p 1365) often manages to survive, but the larger and more conspicuous pigtail gets shot or otherwise squeezed out. Irwin Bernstein, studying monkeys in Malaya, came across an interesting situation in a highly cultivated area. A crabeater troop survived in a forest isolated among the fields, and thrived on crop-raiding; among the crabeaters were two monkeys which were obviously hybrids between crabeaters and pigtails. Quite clearly, the pigtails that had inhabited the forest had been almost exterminated, and the one or two survivors had been forced to join a troop of crabeaters with which they freely interbred. Finally they too were killed, and only these hybrids remained to show that pigtails had ever been there at all.

class	**Mammalia** K Tanaka
order	**Primates**
family	**Cercopithecidae**
genus & species	*Macaca nemestrina* pigtailed monkey *M. silenus* liontailed monkey

*Summing up the situation. An Asiatic pika **Ochotona hyperborea** with its small rounded ears flattened back, hesitatingly emerges from its hiding place among the rock crevices. Its main hope of safety lies in remaining hidden from the weasels, small carnivores and hawks that prey on it.*

Pika

Pikas are small mammals related to the rabbits and hares. They are known by a variety of names, including mouse-hares, rock rabbits, rock conies, calling hares, piping hares and whistling hares. There are two species in North America and 12 in Asia; the largest is a foot long, the smallest less than half this. They look like rabbits or hares with short rounded ears, tailless and with the four legs more or less the same length. Each foot has five toes, and the soles of the feet are hairy, enabling them to run easily over smooth rock surfaces. The fur of pikas is usually greyish brown above and lighter on the underparts, but is reddish in one species. In general the coat is lighter coloured in dry areas, darker in more humid regions. Some species have two moults a year giving a summer coat that is reddish or yellowish and a grey winter coat.

The North American pikas live in and around the Rockies, in the Sierra Nevada, Utah and New Mexico and southeastern Alaska and the Yukon in the north. In Asia they range from the Volga and Urals to Korea and the Japanese island of Hokkaido, and in southern Asia from Persia to Nepal.

From lowlands to Mount Everest

One species of pika lives on Mount Everest up to 17 500 ft, the highest altitude at which any mammal has been found. Pikas live in a variety of habitats; on plains, in deserts, in forests and on rocky mountainsides. One of their most noticeable features is their voice which is usually a whistle or a sharp bark, ca-ak, repeated many times. Both calls are remarkably ventriloquial, the body being jerked forwards and upwards at each cry. Pikas rely for safety on remaining hidden, dropping into a crevice and there lying still. Among rocky screes they use the crevices and cavities as shelters, while on the plains they burrow.

Making hay while the sun shines

Pikas usually live in places where the winters are cold but they do not hibernate. Instead they have the remarkable habit of cutting vegetation with their chisel-like teeth, drying it in the sun and storing it for winter fodder. A pika may travel several hundred feet from home to cut herbs and grass, carrying these in its mouth to a chosen spot to dry, adding a fresh layer each day. Some climb into the lower branches of young trees to take young green shoots. In winter bark is sometimes eaten as the pikas tunnel under snow, but the main food even then is the dry fodder. This is stored under an overhanging shelf of rock or under a fallen tree, a single store holding a bushel of hay. Pikas feed in the early morning and late afternoon. Midday is spent basking. During the day the droppings are small, green and dry. At night they are black and wrapped in a jelly-like layer which keeps them soft and wet. These are swallowed again and kept in the stomach to be mixed with fresh food and redigested, a habit first noticed in rabbits. It has been found that if rabbits are prevented from eating their soft night droppings they will die in about 3 weeks as the droppings are their only source of certain essential vitamins, formed by the activity of bacteria breaking down partly digested plant material in the droppings.

The miners of the Yukon and elsewhere in the western half of North America called the pika the starved rat. Although strictly vegetarian they must, nevertheless, be well fed and far from deserving this nickname. Animals in the north temperate regions can stand up to cold so long as they are well fed. It is not the hard winters that kill but food shortages due to freezing up. Pikas keep going even when the ground is covered with snow, because they have their food stores. They even sun themselves on rocks in temperatures of −17°C/0°F!

Small naked babies

The breeding season is May—September, when each female may have 2 or 3 litters. The gestation period is 30 days and there are 3—5 babies in a litter. Each is born naked and helpless and is put in a nest of dried grass. They weigh 1 oz at birth against

the 1 lb weight of the adults, but reach full size in 6—7 weeks, having been weaned when about a quarter grown. The life span of the pika is 1—3 years and during that time their enemies are weasels and other small carnivores, and hawks.

A modern guinea pig?

Pikas enjoyed a measure of obscurity for a long time, but they now look like emerging to fame as laboratory animals. They were first discovered in North America in about 1828, and the naturalist Thomas Nuttal has left us a record of how he heard, in the Rockies, 'a slender but very distinct bleat, like that of a young kid or goat. But in vain I tried to discover any large animal around me'. Finally he located the little animal 'nothing much larger than a mouse'. Pallas discovered the first pika in Asia in 1769 and although he, and others after him, found species after species in the mountainous parts of Asia and on the steppes, little more was known of them except what they looked like, together with their habit of storing hay and their ventriloquial voice, until about a quarter of a century ago. Since then scientists in the USSR have been paying a lot of attention to them. This is not because they are a nuisance, for they live in out-of-the-way places where they do not clash with man's interests, but because they have all the advantages of the guinea pig as a laboratory animal: they are easy to feed and maintain, inoffensive, and they do not need much room.

class	**Mammalia**
order	**Lagomorpha**
family	**Ochotonidae**
genus & species	*Ochotona pallasi* Pallas' pika *O. princeps* Rocky Mountain pika *O. wollastoni* Mount Everest pika others

△ *One of the many Russian pikas* **Ochotona pusilla** — *a compact, tailless bundle of fur.* ▽ *An all weather animal:* **Ochotona collaris** *in its winter coat.*

Pike

The pike, aptly nicknamed the 'freshwater shark', is the fiercest predatory fish in the fresh waters of the northern hemisphere. It and its relatives, the pickerel and muskellunge of North America, are held in awe by some fishermen, contempt by others; to many they present a challenge, backed by the legends of size and ferocity—often very tall stories. The record of the largest pike caught is of a 53lb specimen.

Ambush

Pike live in still and running water, spending most of their time motionless among water plants with which their colours harmonize. The pike usually stay in one place and dart out to ambush their prey. Having the dorsal and anal fins set far back on the body gives great thrust to the tail and rapid acceleration, sending the pike out 20—30 ft to seize prey. A pike detects its prey by sight rather than by smell, at distances of up to 50 ft by day, but is probably warned of its approach by vibrations in the water, for a blind pike can also catch food. A pike can see at night the pike's teeth. Those on the sides of the lower jaw are strong and stick straight up. They are used for seizing prey. The teeth of the upper jaw are smaller, most numerous in the front, and are curved backwards. The roof of the mouth is bristling with teeth pointing backwards, and these prevent prey slipping out of the mouth. The mouth itself has a wide gape. Sometimes large prey may become jammed in the pike's throat with fatal results for the pike, which cannot get rid of it because of the backwardly directed teeth. Large prey successfully swallowed takes a long time to

Ambush: a northern pike in hiding. It will wait here until prey is near enough for it to dart out rapidly to seize an unsuspecting fish.

A Niestle: Bavaria

The pike—or northern pike, as it is known in North America—is long bodied with a large flat, almost shovel-shaped head with large jaws and large mouth bristling with teeth. Its dorsal and anal fins are set far back. Its colour ranges from olive to dark green with pale yellow spots. It grows up to 4½ ft long and weighs up to 53 lb. The muskellunge of the Great Lakes is very like the pike but has scales on only the upper part of the cheek instead of all over it. It grows to 8 ft long and can weigh up to 110 lb. The grass pickerel, from Nova Scotia to Texas, grows up to 2 ft long, and has dark bands on the flanks. The smaller chain pickerel of the eastern United States grows up to 14 in. long and has a chain-like network of dark markings on the side. The black-spotted pike, which is sometimes called the black-spotted pickerel, lives in eastern Siberia, and very little seems to be known about this fifth member of the family.

as well as by day. Its habit is to lie well down in the water because its eyes are set in the top of the head and look mainly forwards and upwards. It has two sighting grooves running to the tip of the snout. A pike's brain is relatively very small, $\frac{1}{1305}$ of the total body weight, much of this being taken up by the optic lobes. This reflects the little effort the pike needs to make a living.

Gin trap jaws

When very small, pike feed on water fleas, worms and the fry of other fishes. As they grow they take progressively larger fish and are less and less tempted by small prey unless it comes so close they can snap it up without moving. They are almost exclusively fish-eaters, especially of fishes belonging to the carp family Cyprinidae and trout. Large pike will also take other water dwellers such as ducks, moorhens, coots, water voles and frogs. There are many authenticated reports of pike eating prey their own size. This is possible no matter how much it struggles because of

digest, and after a big meal the pike lies inert for a week or more, often near the bottom, taking no notice of prey or the fisherman's bait. A pike can take in large prey because its intestine is more or less straight, its stomach being merely a dilatation of the front part of it.

Unusual digestive juices?

A hungry pike will seize prey of a certain size depending on its own size and usually providing its quarry does not move too slowly, although an angler will catch a pike using stationary dead bait. Pike learn, however, not to go after sticklebacks once they have had experience of their spines. It is sometimes said that the digestive juices of a pike 'are phenomenal', because even hooks are eaten away by its stomach acids. This is, in fact, illusory. When digesting a fish the pike's acidity is high on the surface of the prey, very low inside it, and a pike takes 3—5 days to digest a moderately sized fish. A similar high acidity on the surface of a hook would soon erode it.

High egg wastage

Pike spawn from February to May, the younger individuals spawning first. They are stimulated to spawn by the increasing day length and light intensity. They assemble in shallow water, each female attended by several males. Estimates of the number of eggs laid by each female vary from 40 000 to 500 000, the number depending probably on the size of the female. Many fail to be fertilised because the micropyle, the hole in the egg membrane through which the sperms enter, closes 30−60 seconds after they are laid. At first the eggs are sticky and lie singly on the bottom, later rising just off the bottom. They hatch after 2−3 weeks, the larvae feeding on the remains of the yolk sac for 10 days, before starting to catch their own food. The parents take no care of their eggs or young.

Automatic control of numbers

As pike are at the apex of a food pyramid they probably have few enemies except when very young. There is, however, considerable cannibalism which keeps a proper balance. The more richly a water is stocked with other fish the less the cannibalism; and the end result is that pike are seldom so numerous as to deplete the waters, in which they live, of other fish.

Methuselah pike

Most pike live about 7 years once they have survived the massacre of infancy but they have been known to live 10 years or more and Dr C Tate Regan once asserted that possibly 'fish of sixty or seventy pounds weight are at least as many years old'. There have, however, been many exaggerated claims, like the one, first told by Gesner in 1558, about the famous Emperor's Pike. This pike was supposed to have been caught in a lake in Württemburg in 1497 with a copper ring round its gill region with an inscription saying it had been placed in the lake by the Emperor Frederick II in 1230. So it would have been more than 260 years old. What was not explained was why the ring fitted it so well as pike continue to grow until they die. Had it been put on 260 years before the ring would surely have been a tight fit by 1497.

The pike was said to have been 19 ft long and to weigh 550 lb, and there was a painting of it in the castle of Lautern in Swabia. What appears to be a copy of this still hangs in the British Museum (Natural History). Its skeleton is said to have been preserved in the cathedral in Mannheim. When scientists studied it in the 19th century it was found to have too many vertebrae in its backbone!

class	**Pisces**
order	**Salmoniformes**
family	**Esocidae**
genus & species	*Esox americanus* grass pickerel *E. lucius* northern pike *E. masquinongy* muskellunge *E. niger* chain pickerel *E. reicherti* black spotted pike

◁ *Gin trap jaws: a pike can eat prey its own size with the help of its well appointed dental set.*

Barry Pengilley

Pilchard

Like its relative, the herring, the species, **Sardina pilchardus,** is highly exploited by man—as a sardine when young and a pilchard when adult. The young fish support an extensive canning industry in France, Spain and Portugal; the adults are best known for the pilchard fishery which formerly flourished off Cornwall. The commercial division into sardine and pilchard arises from the geographical races of the species and the extensive migrations.

An adult pilchard is a silvery fish, shaped like a herring but a little smaller and slightly fatter, growing up to 10 in. long. Its dorsal fin is slightly forward of the midline of the body instead of more or less at the centre, as in the herring (p 1063). Its scales, also, are larger than those of a herring. Otherwise the two are very alike. As in the herring the scales are deciduous. That is they lie in shallow pockets on the surface and are easily rubbed off.

The pilchard is divided into northern, southern, Moroccan and Mauretanian races. The first may go into the North Sea, as far north as Northumberland, although it rarely goes farther east than Plymouth, in the English Channel. Southwards it ranges to the Cantabrian coast of Spain. The second ranges from Cantabria to Cadiz, the third from Morocco to Rio de Oro on the bulge of Africa, and the fourth, a dwarf race, from Rio de Oro to Dakar in West Africa. There is a Mediterranean subspecies **S. pilchardus sardina.** The closely related genus **Sardinops** has two species with several subspecies: **S. sagax sagax** lives off the coasts of Chile and Peru, **S. sagax melanosticta** off Japan, **S. sagax ocellatus** off South Africa, and **S. sagax neopilchardus** off the southern half of Australia and around New Zealand. A second species **Sardinops caerulea** lives off the Pacific coast of the United States.

Tinned shoals

Pilchards live in enormous shoals with the individual fishes arranged in echelon. The shoals are made up of fishes of approximately the same size—that is, in age groups—which is a great convenience to man because they sort themselves out naturally for canning! The shoals swim at differing depths during the day and night since they tend to follow the vertical migrations of plankton. By means of very fine gill-rakers the fish sieve even small diatoms from the water passing into the mouth and throat and out by the gills and pick off large numbers of copepods and other planktonic crustaceans. In summer these form the bulk of their food. There is a good deal of variation in the weight of the fish compared with its length, due to the amount of fat in its body. Pilchard feed most from April to July and again in October, when they are heaviest. From November to February or March they fast, taking at most only a very little food.

Drift-netting

Vast shoals are bound to be preyed upon by many predatory fish and seabirds, but the greatest predator is man. The sardines react to attacks from fish and birds by swimming together and milling around in large tight and compact balls, a defence that would be useless against the drift-nets and seines used by fishermen. For pilchards, for example, the nets are shot at sunset, fastened end to end, with one end attached by a rope to the bows of a boat, nets and boat then drifting with the tide.

Identification by balance

Shakespeare seems to have believed that 'Fools are as like Husbands, as Pilchers (pilchards) are to Herrings'. The standard way of discriminating between a herring, pilchard and sprat is to hold each by its dorsal fin. The herring hangs horizontally because the fin is at the centre of the back. In the pilchard it is nearer the head, so the tail dips, and in the sprat it is nearer the tail, so its nose drops. In fact, herring and pilchard are so alike there has even been talk of their hybridizing, and fishes are caught that look very like hybrids. They have 30 rows of scales along one side of the body and 50 along the other. The explanation is that pilchards have oblique rows of alternately large and small scales. In a normal pilchard the small scales are hidden by the large ones. In the hybrid the scales of one side are all large, while those on the other side are large and small.

class	**Pisces**
order	**Clupeiformes**
family	**Clupeidae**
genus & species	**Sardina pilchardus**

◁ Thousands of pilchards schooling on the Barrier Reef bring order out of confusion as they gather in a clockwise direction into a school. The fish will arrange themselves in echelon and each school consists of fish of approximately the same size.

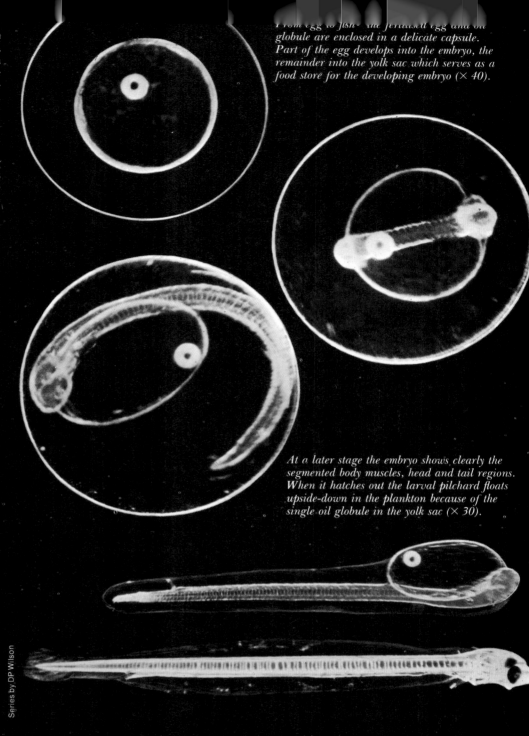

Preferred spawning temperatures

The spawning is from April to July when each female lays up to 60 000 large eggs, 20–40 miles from shore, in waters with a temperature of 10–17°C/50–63°F. The eggs are peculiar in having a large space between the egg itself and the outer membrane. This, with the large globule of oil each contains, makes the eggs buoyant and they float at the surface. The larvae hatch in days or so, each being ½ in. long.

The temperature needed for spawning differs for each race of pilchard but lies between the limits already quoted. In the northern race there are two distinct populations. One spawns south of Cornwall, sometimes in the English Channel as far east as Dover, or off the coast of Brittany, the young fishes then migrating south to the level of St Jean-de-Luz where they stay for years before migrating northwards to spawn on the grounds where they were hatched. They are fished as sardines off the west coast of France and the north coast of Spain, and as pilchards off Cornwall. The second population spawns in the Bay of Biscay, the young fish from these eggs spending their first 2 years in the same place, after which they migrate north as mature fish (pilchards) and do not return to their birthplace.

In the southern race the young fish, 2 years of age or less, are found off Portugal, the 2–6 year olds being found off the north coast of Spain. In the Moroccan race the young are found off Agadir and the adults off Safi.

Spawning and post-spawning migrations take place from November to June from Gibraltar to Galicia, from November to April from Santander in Spain to Areachon in France, from February to July off Brittany and from April to November in the Celtic Sea—the area west and southwest of Cornwall. The appearance from south to north of shoals of adults following the successive spawning periods gave rise to the idea that there was an extensive south-north migration, whereas it is only a succession of small migrations of local populations.

The unassuming pilchard is an important source of food especially in Spain and Portugal. Like the herring it has soft-rayed fins, and the scales along the belly are easily rubbed off.

Series by DP Wilson

From egg to fish—the fertilised egg and oil globule are enclosed in a delicate capsule. Part of the egg develops into the embryo, the remainder into the yolk sac which serves as a food store for the developing embryo (× 40).

At a later stage the embryo shows clearly the segmented body muscles, head and tail regions. When it hatches out the larval pilchard floats upside-down in the plankton because of the single oil globule in the yolk sac (× 30).

Ludwig Sillner

Shark's jackal? Pilot fishes swim alongside a whitetip shark **Carcharhinus longimanus.** *It was believed that pilot fishes guided sharks and rays towards suitable prey, receiving in return protection from enemies because of their closeness to a formidable companion. In reality, however, both fishes are in search of food, the pilot no doubt benefiting from the efforts of its big companion but never leading the foray.*

Fatal shelter

So little is known for certain about the way of life of pilot fishes, and what is known seems extraordinary. It is always supposed that by swimming under the bells of jellyfishes or among the tentacles the baby pilot fishes are protected from enemies. This may be true but they are also exposed to the dangers of being eaten by animals which feed on jellyfishes. These are more numerous than one would think. They include seabirds, such as frigate birds and fulmars and the large fishes, including the large ocean sunfishes. Indeed, there must be the suspicion that these animals may be taking the jellyfishes more for the fishes sheltering under them since jellyfishes are 99% water.

Why follow sharks?

There is also uncertainty about the protection a pilot fish gets from swimming near a shark. It is usually taken for granted that it does get protection because the shark itself is so voracious that potential enemies are unlikely to come near, but a pilot fish would get no protection from swimming with a whale or a shoal of tunny, less still from a bunch of Sargasso weed, a piece of floating wreckage or a sailing ship. We know that pilot fishes sometimes travel inside the mouths of large rays which do not eat fish. It may be they sometimes enter the mouths of sharks—but do not live to serve as evidence! All the signs are that pilot fishes have the instinct to swim near a body larger than themselves; when young it is a jellyfish, when adult it is anything from a shark to a schooner. The very early idea that they are friendly to man is not far from the truth if by being friendly we mean they like to keep close to us—or to our ships.

The researches of the Soviet scientist VV Shuleikin, published about 1957, give the only valid reason for pilot fishes swimming beside sharks and ships. Shuleikin calculated that sharks swim three times as fast as a pilot fish possibly can. How then does a pilot fish keep up? Over the surface of any body moving through water there is a 'boundary layer' of water moving forward at almost the same speed as that of the body. This is thickest over the tail half of a shark, which is where a pilot fish usually swims. So presumably the pilot fish is able to travel hundreds of miles in a boundary layer carried along by it, with a minimum of effort.

Pilot fish

The pilot fish is so named because it was believed to guide sharks and whales, and to lead ships or solitary swimmers to land or to a port when they had lost their way. These beliefs go back at least to the time of the Ancient Greeks.

The pilot fish can grow up to 2 ft long. It has a strongly forked tail that is blackish with white tips, a prominent dorsal fin with 4 strong spines in front of it, a prominent anal fin and small pectoral and pelvic fins. Its body is marked with 5—7 dark bands, brownish to black, on a background of white to bluish-white. It is widespread through tropical and temperate seas and is occasionally caught off the coasts of the British Isles.

Social hangers-on

So far as one can tell, pilot fish do nothing else than swim about in company with large sharks, whales, giant mantas, large schools of tunny and sailing ships. They have sometimes been caught in mackerel and herring nets. Although the ancient belief is that they lead, and therefore guide or act as pilots, they more commonly swim at the side or even follow other fish. Nevertheless, the association is a very persistent one. Pilot fishes accompanying a shark which is then hooked and hauled on board ship have swum around its tail, the last part of the shark to leave the water, as if distracted. Again, a pilot fish is recorded as following a sailing ship continuously for 80 days. The idea that they piloted a ship to port was fostered to some extent by the way the fish

left it as it neared land or after it had entered harbour. One explanation for this, which does not seem unreasonable, is that they turn away when they feel the freshwater brought down by rivers.

Why pilot fishes should accompany large animals and other objects is something of a mystery. One explanation put forward is that, with their better eyesight, they see food before the shark does and lead it to it, taking the scraps as the shark feeds. This is, however, almost entirely guesswork dating at least from the 16th century when pilot fishes were called the sharks' jackals. What seems more certain is that a pilot fish may suddenly dart from a shark's side to snap up something, but it quickly returns to take up station once more. On the few occasions that pilot fishes have been caught and their stomachs examined they seem to have been eating small fishes rather than scraps of food.

Different babies

Spawning seems to take place in the early summer well away from land. It is always said that the eggs float at or near the surface but a note from the Soviet scientist AI Svetovidov, published in 1958, says that pilot fishes always lay their eggs on the skin of sharks or the submerged hulls of ships. The parents then stay with the eggs until they hatch. The larvae hatching from them are so unlike the parent that they were originally thought to belong to a separate species. They have large eyes and numerous spines on the head, and they shelter under the bells of jellyfishes and among the tentacles of the Portuguese man-o'-war, under bunches of Sargasso weed and pieces of floating wreckage.

class	**Pisces**
order	**Perciformes**
family	**Carangidae**
genus & species	*Naucrates ductor*

Pilot whale

*Also called the blackfish or caa'ing whale,
the pilot whale is a dolphin that can
grow to 28 ft long. Its most distinctive
feature, from which it gets its scientific
name of* **Globicephala,** *is the bulging
forehead, which forms a dome overhanging the mouth. The upward curve of
the mouth gives it an amused look. The
tapered flippers are long, about ⅕ of the
total body length. The dorsal fin stands
about 1 ft high. Pilot whales are black
except for a white patch under the chin.*

*Pilot whales are found in many parts
of the world but are absent from the polar
seas.* **Globicephala melaena** *of the North
Atlantic and Mediterranean ranges as far
north as Greenland. It is common off the
Faeroes, Shetland and Orkney.*
G. macrorhyncha *is found in the Caribbean
and off the southeast seaboard of the United
States.* **G. scammoni** *lives in the Pacific
Ocean. The last two species have shorter
fins than* **G. melaena.**

Mass suicide

Pilot whales live in large schools sometimes
numbering hundreds, or even thousands.
Each school is made up of both males and
females and it has often been reported that
a male acts as a leader. This is presumably
how these animals got their name, but it is
more likely that there is a general tendency
to follow any individual. Hunters have
found that when one pilot whale is wounded
and rushes away, the other members of the
school follow it. A dolphin named Pelorus
Jack, that regularly followed ships plying
between Wellington and Nelson, New
Zealand, for 20 years, may have been a pilot
whale exhibiting its following habit. On the
other hand, some writers think that Pelorus
Jack, who had the distinction of worldwide
fame and protection under Order in Coun-
cil, was a Risso's dolphin *Grampus griseus*.
The habit of following a leader has, however, made schools of pilot whales very
susceptible to become stranded. If one
whale, perhaps becoming panic-stricken
at finding itself in shallow water, goes
ashore, the others follow like sheep. Attempts have sometimes been made to refloat
stranded pilot whales, but they have failed.
As soon as one whale is dragged into
deeper water, it swims back to the shore.
Presumably the rescued whales are blindly
answering the calls of the stranded ones.
Killer whales behave in the same way.

Blind hunting

Pilot whales are armed with 7–11 teeth in each side of each jaw. These are used for grabbing slippery prey, which is mainly squid and cuttlefish, but fish are also taken. The eyesight of pilot whales is not good and their bulbous heads and inflexible necks must prevent them from seeing objects directly ahead, so perhaps they use sound waves to find food like other dolphins.

Warm water breeding

Sightings of pilot whale schools over many years show that they migrate regularly. The migrations are partly regulated by food supply, as when pilot whales move to the coast of Newfoundland in summer after the squid *Illex,* but there is a more general movement to warmer waters in winter. It appears that mating takes place in the warmer waters and calves are born when the pilot whales return to cooler regions in the following year.

It is usual for whales to migrate to warmer seas to breed, as does the blue whale (p 248) for instance, for newborn whales have very little insulating blubber. To compensate for this the whale's milk is extremely rich, having only 40–50% water, half as much as cow's milk. The fat content of whale's milk is very high 40–50%, that of cows is only about 4%.

Until observations were made in oceanaria, very little was known about the mating habits of whales, but pilot whales had been seen courting in the wild. The partners have been seen stroking each other with their flippers or bodies as they swim slowly past and on one occasion the mate of a weather ship watched the amorous antics of about 20 pilot whales. They were swimming side by side in pairs, playfully biting each other's mouths, and surfacing vertically until their flippers were exposed. They would then submerge and lie belly to belly for about 20 seconds, copulation in whales being extremely rapid.

Female pilot whales start to breed when 6 years old and bear young in alternate years. They are barren at 18 years. Males mature in 13 years. Pilot whales are thought to live for a maximum of about 50 years.

Orgy of slaughter

For hundreds of years pilot whales have been hunted in the islands to the north of the British Isles. The hunts, which are still carried on in the Faeroes, but have ceased in Orkney and Shetland, depend on a school of pilot whales being sighted near the shore. The alarm is given and a fleet of small boats puts out to carefully shepherd the school into a bay. The whales panic and rush

△ *Letting off steam? A Pacific pilot whale* **Globicephala scammoni** *surfaces, 'blowing its nose' as it breathes out. The whale's spout is not water. Whales can submerge for more than half an hour and can tolerate an increase of carbon-dioxide in the blood during this time. Previous page: Follow-the-leader; a school of pilot whales, identified by high dorsal fins.*

into the shallows. Men from the boats and those waiting on the shore immediately set on the whales with knives and lances.

When the slaughter is over the carcases are stripped of their blubber. The division of the spoils follows a strict tradition. Certain proportions are awarded to the man who first spotted the whales, those who went out in the boats, the men who helped in the slaughter and so on. A share is also put aside for the poor. The capture of a school of pilot whales, was an absolute windfall to the islanders, and even now there are wild scenes following the slaughter of *grindehval,* as the Faeroese call them.

class	**Mammalia**
order	**Cetacea**
family	**Delphinidae**
genus & species	***Globicephala melaena*** *others*

Pink-footed goose

The pink-footed goose is a small variety of the bean goose. The latter is so-named because it arrives in England in October, at the time of the bean harvest and then stays to feed on the beans left lying in the fields. There are two basic types of bean goose; the forest bean geese have long, slender bills, while the tundra bean geese, stockier birds, have shorter deeper bills. The pink-footed geese are the latter type. Their length from bill to tail is 24-30 in. The head and neck are dark brown, the underparts light pinkish brown and the wings and tail ash grey with white edgings. The feet are pink and so is the bill except the base and tip, although it may very occasionally be wholly pink.

Bean geese breed in the tundra and forest zones, from Greenland to eastern Siberia, but the pink-footed goose is restricted to eastern Greenland, Iceland and Spitzbergen. In the winter they migrate to Britain, northern France, Belgium, Holland and Germany. They occasionally turn up in North America, Russia and other parts of Europe.

Wary geese

During the winter pink-footed geese gather in very large flocks on sandbanks, moors, in estuaries, flooded marshes and around coasts—all places where they are unlikely to be disturbed. As is usual with geese, pink-foots are extremely wary and difficult to approach. Pink-footed geese arrive in their winter quarters in September and October, having migrated from the breeding grounds, with only a few stops, in the Faeroes or Scandinavia. They fly in skeins of over 1 000 geese with family parties of adults and goslings keeping together. When they arrive, weary and hungry, they are less wary than usual and for a few days it is possible to get nearer to them before they recover their strength. The flocks stay south until April or May.

Grazing and gleaning

In the autumn and winter pink-footed geese feed in stubble fields, usually of barley, but they also eat young wheat and grass stems. On the breeding grounds they eat buds, stalks, seeds and leaves of many plants including willow, sedge, horsetails, chickweed and grasses.

Safe nesting places

By the time the pink-footed geese have reached the breeding grounds they have already paired off. All arrive within a few days and only a few more days elapse before the eggs are laid. Most pairs nest in loose colonies but some raise their broods singly, especially in the open tundra. If large numbers nested together in open country predators such as Arctic foxes would be attracted to such easy prey with devastating

▽ *Pink-footed goose in profile.*

results. The colonies are usually in more inaccessible places such as the talus, the piles of boulders that form at the bottom of cliffs, on moraines, cliff ledges or terraces. Some colonies are on islands in rivers. When on level ground the nests are built on hillocks or frost mounds where the sitting bird can get a good view of the surrounding country. The gander usually keeps a watch from a lookout point nearby.

The nest is a depression in the ground lined with grasses and other plants and with a considerable quantity of down. The 4–5 eggs, sometimes more, are incubated by the goose alone while the gander stands guard. The eggs hatch in just under 4 weeks. The chicks leave the nest within 48 hours and never return. Their parents lead them down to water when they leave the nest and a new roost is used each night.

The adults moult during the breeding season, shedding all their feathers simultaneously so they cannot fly until the new ones regrow. As soon as they and their young can fly, they migrate south.

Moments of danger

When they have moulted their flight feathers they are helpless and although the natural wariness of geese usually keeps them relatively safe from enemies, unless they are in an isolated place they will fall prey to Arctic foxes. Greater black-backed gulls, Iceland falcons, white-tailed eagles and Arctic foxes are also known to prey on the eggs and chicks of pink-footed geese in Iceland.

Goose round up

The Arctic breeding grounds of pink-footed geese are a comparatively recent discovery. The birds were first discovered breeding in Spitzbergen in 1855 and in Greenland in 1891. The colonies there were fairly small and many years passed before the main colonies in Iceland were discovered. The first clues came in 1921, but proof was obtained in 1951 when Peter Scott, James Fisher and Finnur Gudmundson travelled to the interior of Iceland and found over 2 000 nests at an oasis on a high plain. They ringed over 1 000 pink-footed geese to find where they spent the winter, catching them by driving them into nets. At that time of the year neither adults nor goslings could fly so they were easy to capture. Nearby they found the remains of U-shaped stone walls 36 ft long and 6 ft across the entrance. These were the ruins of goose pens that had been used by the Icelanders centuries before for rounding up flightless geese. Of course their purpose in capturing them was not for the study of the birds or their migration but to fill up their larders.

class	**Aves**
order	**Anseriformes**
family	**Anatidae**
genus & species	*Anser fabalis brachyrhynchus*

▽ *Winter feeding-grounds—pink-footed geese graze the stubble on a field in northern Europe.*

Pintail

The pintail is probably the most numerous duck in the world. It is the same length as a mallard, 22 in., except that the central pair of tail feathers are elongated, forming the pin-tail which may be as much as 4 in. long in males. The plumage of the male is distinctive, with a blackish-brown head and neck, and with a white collar running down the side of the neck and across the breast. The back and belly are patterned and there is a patch of white on the belly in front of a patch of black at the base of the tail. The female is very much like a mallard duck. The male goes into eclipse from mid-July to early September. The eclipse plumage is like that of the female but is darker on the upper parts and the 'speculum' of bronzy-green with a buff bar on the front, can be seen on the wings.

The pintail is distributed around the northern hemisphere and it migrates south in winter.

The Bahama pintail ranges from the Bahamas through most of South America and also breeds on the Galapagos islands. It has distinctive white patches on the sides of its face. Some pintails breed farther south than any other duck. There are subspecies of the northern pintail on the sub-Antarctic islands of Kerguelen and the Crozets, and South Georgia has its own separate species. These sub-Antarctic pintails are confusingly called teal; and, to add to the confusion, the males are in eclipse plumage all the year round.

Habitat destroyed

The vast inhospitable wastes of the Arctic tundra provide the breeding ground for the pintail which nests in the numerous scattered pools and lakes. Freshwater pools are preferred to brackish ones, and nests are not usually found on water surrounded by marshy ground. In the Galapagos there are very few stretches of freshwater where the Bahama pintail can live. A few years ago a large lake in a volcanic crater on the island of Fernandina was destroyed by an eruption, so robbing the Galapagos pintail population of most of their habitat. In Europe pintail prefer wintering around coasts and estuaries, whilst in India large numbers are found on inland lakes. This is unusual as pintail are usually seen in only small numbers on inland waters. On the sea, however, they may form flocks of over 1000, these large flocks being split up into small parties which mingle with other ducks rather than forming tightly-packed rafts.

Rarely dive

Pintail feed by paddling in the shallows, upending, or by uprooting water plants such as pond weed, sedge and dock. Acorns and grain from stubble, beetles, fly larvae, worms

▷ *Pintail silhouettes.*

Arthur Christiansen

and tadpoles are also taken. Their winter diet includes seaweed and eelgrass. Pintail do not dive except to escape danger when unable to fly while moulting during eclipse or because of wounds.

Female distractions
The display courtship of the pintail is similar to that of the mallard (p 1382) and there are aerial pursuits in which the female is chased by several males. Pintail often perform aerial dives, plunging at an angle of 45° from a great height, stooping with their wings stiffly outspread and slightly curved down. Just before hitting the ground they level out and glide a few yards off the ground for 100–300 yd.

The greatest concentrations of breeding pintails are probably in the tundra of Alaska where every small pool houses one or more pairs. Elsewhere the nests are fairly close together, sometimes a long way from water. These are no more than a down-lined hollow in the ground among marram grass, heather, rushes or other low plants. The 7–9 eggs are incubated by the female, and usually guarded by the male. The chicks

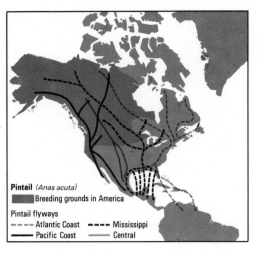

Pintail (*Anas acuta*)
■ Breeding grounds in America
Pintail flyways
--- Atlantic Coast   ----- Mississippi
—— Pacific Coast   —— Central

△ *Pintail breed throughout the northern hemisphere in Asia, northern Europe, including Britain, Iceland and central and western Canada.*

▽ *Sitting duck. A female pintail on her nest, a down-lined hollow in the grass. The favourite pintail breeding grounds are in the Arctic tundra, around the many scattered pools.*

hatch out after 22–23 days and shortly afterwards are led to the nearest water to feed. If disturbed, the chicks hide among water plants, and there are records of their mother performing distraction displays in which she approaches close to the intruder, and splashes about vigorously, swimming in circles. The young fly when 5–7 weeks old.

Aerial highways

Ducks of the genus *Anas*, to which the pintail and mallard belong, make up three-quarters of the quarry of wildfowlers. In the United States in particular, vast numbers of wildfowl are shot every year as they fly across the country to and from the breeding grounds in the north. To protect the waterfowl there are stringent game laws and conservation agencies prepare suitable stretches of water for the birds to settle. Their task is made easier because the waterfowl, as well as other birds, travel along traditional routes.

Migrating birds usually take the line of least resistance. Birds of prey, for instance, cross the Mediterranean by the shortest sea routes, over the Straits of Gibraltar and the Bosphorus. Sometimes, however, the only way is over difficult ground. Pintails migrating in and out of India have to cross mountains, and the skeleton of one was found 16 000 ft up Mount Everest. In North America there are four well-defined migration routes that follow geographical features. These were discovered, and named 'flyways' by Frederick Lincoln, from information gathered from banded birds, mainly waterfowl of various species.

The flyways start in the tundra of Alaska and northern Canada, and continue down through the plains of Canada and into the USA. On the way, the ducks and geese from the Arctic are joined by hosts of other birds and finish on winter grounds around the Caribbean Sea or in South America. The most important flyway is that down the Mississippi Valley to the marshy shores of the Gulf of Mexico. Next in importance is the central flyway, also starting in Alaska but then running close to the eastern side of the Rocky Mountains. Along the coasts there are the Atlantic and Pacific flyways, one leading to the West Indies and South America, the other to the Pacific coast of Mexico and California. These flyways are less used because the winter climate of the coasts is less severe than in the centre of the continent. Therefore there is less pressure on the birds to travel south.

Eric Hosking

class	**Aves**
order	**Anseriformes**
family	**Anatidae**
genus & species	***Anas acuta*** pintail ***A. bahamensis*** Bahama pintail ***A. georgicus*** South Georgia pintail

P Morris

◁ *Surface feeder: pintail drake dips its bill. They sometimes upend and they often uproot water plants. The two elongated central tail feathers form its distinctive pintail.*

Pipefish

These eel-like fishes were given their name in the mid-18th century, when pipe stems were long and very thin. Today they would probably have been called pipe-cleaner fish. The shape of the body has led to such names as worm pipefish, snake pipefish and threadfish. There are over 150 species from 1 to 18 in. long, in tropical and temperate seas. All are long and very slender with long heads, tubular mouths and tufted gills. Instead of scales, they have a series of jointed bonelike rings encircling the body, from behind the head to the tip of the tail. Some have a small tailfin, in others there is none. The main fin is in the middle of the back.

The colours of pipefishes are usually dull: greenish or olive, like the seaweeds among which they live. Most have a slight banded pattern, which is particularly well marked in the banded pipefish

Anthony Bannister: NHPA

△ *Pipefish portrait:* **Syngnathus** *shows off its intricate patterning. They often swim in a strange semivertical position with their pectoral fins vibrating so rapidly as to be almost a blur.*

▽ *A group of banded pipefish* **Dunckerocampus caulleryi** *patrol a coral reef off New Caledonia in the South Pacific.*

of New Caledonia. Some are mottled and spotted. Some pipefishes can change colour, like the Florida pipefish, which is normally dark green when among eelgrass but goes light when among pale green weed. Others in American seas are muddy brown but turn brick-red when among red weeds. The sea dragon of Australian coasts has leaf-like flaps and spines, and it looks like a piece of floating seaweed.

Most pipefishes are marine or estuarine and a few are freshwater. The marine species live chiefly inshore, in shallow seas, but some live at depths of 50 ft or more, and one lives among the weed of the Sargasso Sea, off the coast of Florida.

Vertical swimmers

Pipefishes in shallow waters and estuaries often live among eelgrass, the only flowering plant in the sea, with long swordlike leaves. They swim in a vertical position with the dorsal and pectoral fins vibrating in time with each other, driving the fish through the water in a leisurely fashion. The vibra-

tions of the dorsal fin are so rapid as to give the impression of a tiny propeller. They can also slip through the water with snake-like movements of the body. They can turn their heads from side to side, and use these movements for steering. The eyes can be moved independently of each other, as in chameleons. Pipefishes may also be found among seaweeds, at times in rockpools, in holes and crevices, and there are species in tropical seas that live in the interstices in coral rock rubble, almost like earthworms.

Fussy vacuum cleaner

Pipefishes have no teeth and they have been described as suffering from permanent lock-jaw, with the locked jaws supporting the tubular mouth. They cannot pursue prey but do the next best thing. The mouth acts as a syringe and can suck in a small plank-tonic animal from 1½ in. away. When search-ing for food they may swim upright or in a horizontal position, wriggling and twisting the body, turning the head this side and that and thrusting among tufts of weed or into cracks and crevices. They seem to be selective, apparently scrutinizing each cope-pod or other small animal, tasting the mor-sel, and ejecting it forcibly if not satisfied. Some spiny larvae of crabs are inspected but left severely alone.

Sexes swap jobs

The main interest of pipefishes is in their breeding. They are related to sea-horses, the males of which have a pouch in which the female lays her eggs. The pipefishes are less simple. In some species the female merely lays her eggs on the underside of the male and there they stick. At the other extreme are species in which the male has a long pouch formed by folds of the surface growing down and meeting in the middle line. There are grades between the two; in some species there are merely two folds of skin in which the eggs lie. All pipefishes have, however, one thing in common: the male carries the burden of the offspring. In many of them the female does all or most of the courting.

Courtship has been fully studied in the Florida pipefish. The two swim round each other in the vertical position but with the head and front part of the body bent for-ward. They swim in decreasing circles until their bodies touch, when the male bends farther forwards and caresses the female with his snout. He becomes excited, wrig-gling his body in corkscrew fashion as he continues to caress the female with his snout. Finally, their bodies become en-twined, she inserts her ovipositor into his pouch and lays some eggs. The male wriggles his body to work the eggs down into the pouch, after which the female lays more eggs, and this is repeated until the pouch is full. The eggs hatch and the larvae are shot out, one or a few at a time, by the male making convulsive movements. Even when able to swim freely the baby pipefishes may dive back into the pouch in times of danger.

Submarine flirtation

It is not surprising that for a long time the male pipefish should have been mistaken for the female. It was not until 1831 that this

RH Noailles: Jacana

△ *Moment of birth for a father! In some pipe-fish the male carries the developing eggs in a pouch, the female inserting them as the climax to an intimate caressing courtship.*
▽ *Some **Syngnathus griseolineata** have preg-nant pouches seen halfway along their bodies.*

was corrected, and it was many years later before they had been studied sufficiently to show how completely the roles of male and female were reversed, even to the female doing the courting. The female broadnosed pipefish of the Mediterranean, for example, courts the male for several hours before he responds. Then he swings his body from side to side, through a right angle, re-minding one of the wriggling and swaying of the bashful suitor. This facetious idea receives support from the further behaviour of the female of this species who seems to flirt preposterously, courting one male after another, even mating with several in turn.

class	**Pisces**
order	**Gasterosteiformes**
family	**Syngnathidae**
genera & species	***Nerophis aequoreus*** *snake pipefish* ***Phycodurus eques*** *sea dragon* ***Syngnathus acus*** *great pipefish* ***S. floridae*** *Florida pipefish* ***S. typhle*** *broadnosed pipefish* *others*

Pipistrelle

The pipistrelle or common bat, as it is called in Britain, is the most familiar as well as the smallest of European bats, although there are several other species of pipistrelle in continental Europe that are only slightly larger. It is recognisable by its jerky erratic flight and because it appears earlier in the evening than most other bats, sometimes coming out even in broad daylight. The jerky flight of pipistrelles gave rise to the ancient name for bats, which was flittermouse — German **Fledermaus** — and another medieval name for bats was reremouse.

Weighing only $\frac{1}{4}$ oz and with a maximum head and body length of 2 in., the pipistrelle is nevertheless of robust build, with short legs, broad flat head and a tail just over an inch long. The last joint of the tail is free of the interfemoral membrane joining the thighs, and is prehensile; the bat is thought to make use of this joint as a support when crawling up or down a vertical surface. The wingspan is 8—9 in. The calcar, a spur on the hindleg, reaches almost to the tail and behind it is a lobe of membrane, the post-calcarial lobe, an important feature of identification.

Except on the ears and wing-membranes where it is blackish, the somewhat silky fur of the upperparts varies from dark to light reddish brown. The underparts are paler and the undersurface of the inter-femoral membrane has no fur. The muzzle is blunt with a wide mouth, and the short, somewhat triangular, ears, slightly notched on their outer edges, end just behind the angle of the mouth.

There are about 40 species of pipistrelle. The range of the common pipistrelle includes the whole of the British Isles and continental Europe, southwest Asia north-eastwards to Korea and Japan and eastwards to Kashmir, and also Morocco. Other species live in Madagascar, the Malay Archipelago, Australia, the Philippines and North America.

The pipistrelle lives in a wide variety of places, singly or in colonies which may be small or may contain hundreds of bats.

It can be found, for instance, under roofs, behind drainpipes and gutters or in holes in woodwork and brickwork as well as in hollow trees and rock-crevices. Although the pipistrelle hibernates in the colder parts of its range, it is for a short period only: late October or November to March. A temperature rise of about 4—5 Centigrade degrees will awaken it and it will emerge from time to time for an hour's hunt for food. It may also move from one hibernaculum to another during winter.

Do my ears deceive me?

Hunting over a regular beat the pipistrelle flies at between 6 and 40 ft above the ground, uttering its shrill squeaks and capturing its prey on the wing. It feeds mainly on flies, particularly gnats, small beetles and other insects. It was once thought that the pipistrelle continued to hunt throughout the night, but it is more likely that it has periods of activity alternating with rest throughout the night, although it may not return to its roost until an hour or so before sunrise.

The bat uses its eyes to some small extent, but it relies mainly upon echo-location to find its way around and to capture prey. The

△ A resting pipistrelle bares its sharp teeth — good equipment for snapping up insects.
◁ Adult and young common pipistrelles sleep upside-down during the day, clinging on to a wall by their tiny claws.

frequent, ultrasonic squeaks bounce back from any solid object and, by interpreting the time taken for the echo to return, the bat is able to 'see' its surroundings. A bat probably carries a sound-picture of familiar territory, comparable to the visual memory of man. It appears, however, unable to assess size accurately. This is shown by the fact that a pebble tossed up into the path of a hunting pipistrelle will be followed down in an attempt at capture, although the pebble may be larger than the bat.

Delayed conception

Pipistrelles mate shortly before going into hibernation but fertilisation is delayed until the following spring. The single young is born between late June and mid-July after

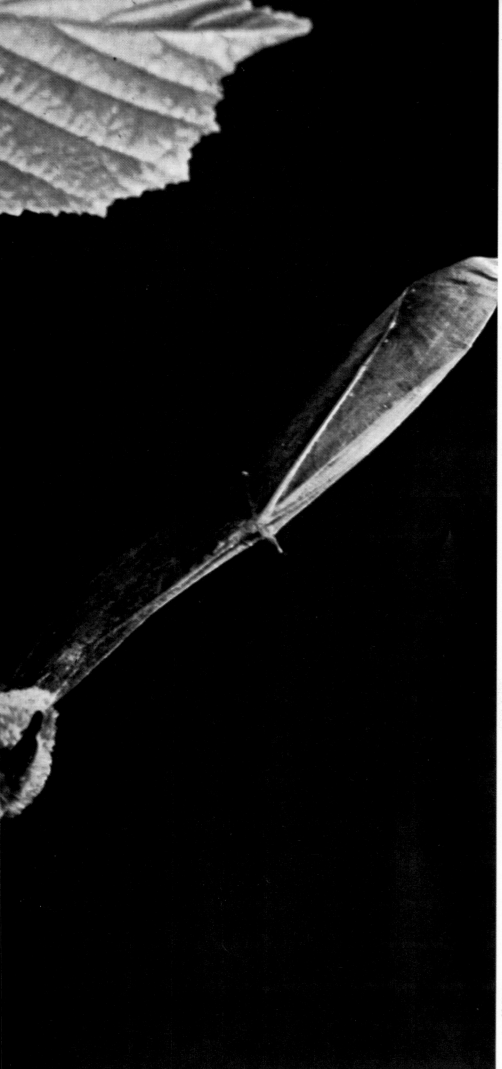

◁ *Wings in the night. The common pipistrelle, the smallest European bat, is one of the first bats to appear in the evening and has a characteristic jerky flight.*

a gestation of 35–44 days. The American eastern pipistrelle has two mating periods, in late summer and early spring, but only one litter results, of 1–3 young, also born in June or July. The females of this species usually form 'maternity colonies' and the young are weaned and ready for independent flight at 3 weeks old.

As in the European species, females of this American species are smaller than the males, which are 3½ in. long, including a 1½-in. tail, have a wingspan of 6 in. and weigh up to ¼ oz. Their fur is yellow-brown above and paler below, with blackish wing-membranes. Their food is chiefly small beetles and flies; larger insects are held in the interfemoral membrane to be eaten. The American western pipistrelle is similar in appearance and habits but is found westward from the Rockies to the Pacific coast.

Drinking on the wing

Although pipistrelles eat mainly insects, whose bodies contain 70% water, they do need to drink, a fact which often escapes the attention of those unaccustomed to seeing bats anywhere near ground level. Moreover, the pipistrelle's choice for hibernation is often a cave or similar hiding place where the air is humid, sometimes so much so that their bodies become beaded with moisture. This damp atmosphere prevents them from becoming dehydrated. During the summer, however, their roosts, under roofs for example, are hot and dry and they must drink. To get water pipistrelles use one of two methods. Either they land on the ground, for bats can scuttle like mice although more slowly, or they skim a pond or stream in the manner of swallows and martins, dipping their lower jaw into the water while in flight. A pipistrelle has been observed to do this several times in the course of a few minutes, swooping and manoeuvring over a pond, making use of the wind like a glider pilot.

Although it has been claimed that bats can swim, it is doubtful whether any of them, even the fish-eating bats of tropical America, deliberately take to the water; a strong argument against this claim is the number of bats found drowned annually in water butts. From time to time pipistrelles having landed on water, have been seen to 'row' themselves to shore, using their wings like oars, and there are scattered reports of other small bats doing the same.

class	**Mammalia**
order	**Chiroptera**
family	**Vespertilionidae**
genus & species	***Pipistrellus hesperus*** *American western pipistrelle* ***P. pipistrellus*** *common pipistrelle* ***P. subflavus*** *American eastern pipistrelle* *others*

Pipit

The pipits are a group of more than 50 inconspicuous birds that, together with the wagtails, make up the family Motacillidae. To those who are not bird watchers pipits are just little brown birds, and if any attention is paid to them they are probably dismissed as sparrows. Although generally the same brown colour as the house sparrow, pipits have a more elaborate patterning of light and dark brown on the back, head and breast. Both in appearance and habits pipits are more like larks. They live on the ground and some sing in flight. They are small, slender birds, 6—7 in. long, with pointed wings and fairly long legs. The plumage of the different European species is so similar that it is very difficult to identify pipits in the field. Identification is usually only possible by a quality called the 'jizz' of a bird. This is a term used by bird-watchers to describe the individual collection of characters such as size and shape of the body, the proportions of different parts and the colouring that each species possesses.

*Pipits are found on all six continents; even Antarctica is included because of one species **Anthus antarcticus** living on South Georgia, a large island lying within the Antarctic Convergence. Several pipits range over large areas of the northern hemisphere, some migrating as far south as southern Africa and Australia. The meadow pipit A. **pratensis** or titlark is found in most of Europe except in the south, and spreads into northwestern Asia, Iceland and Greenland. The tree pipit A. **trivialis** extends from Europe across central Asia, and the rock pipit A. **spinoletta** is scattered through Europe, Asia and North America. Where it lives on rocky shores it is called the rock pipit, but it is also found in mountain valleys, up to 12 000 ft in the Rockies, and here it is called the water pipit. The Bogota pipit A. **bogotensis** lives up to 14 000 ft in the Andes of Ecuador. The only other North American pipit is Sprague's pipit A. **spraguei** of the prairies. Six species live in South America and at least 11 in Africa. Some of the African species are brightly coloured. The yellow-breasted pipit A. **chloris** has yellow underparts and the golden pipit **Tmetothylacus tenellus** is yellow all over. Also living in Africa are eight species called longclaws. The yellow-throated longclaw **Macronyx croceus** is about 7 in. long and has an exceptionally long hindclaw of 2 in. The hindclaws of other pipits are often long, but not as exaggerated as this.*

Song flights

A tree pipit can often be seen perched right on the top of a tall tree, before it launches

△△ *Tree pipit with finely patterned plumage.*
△ *Orange-throated longclaw* **Macronyx capensis** *with exceptionally long hindclaws.*

into its song flight, flying up almost vertically. Just before it levels out it starts to sing, gliding down with its wings above its head and its tail spread. The song is more elaborate than that of the meadow or rock pipit. It consists of a single phrase of two to four notes, repeated several times and ends with a shrill trill. The soaring flight and repetitive song that carries well is very larklike, but compared with the skylark both the flight and song are very short. Pipits live mainly in open country such as grasslands, pampas, savannah and moorland, although some live in swamps, beside streams or along the shore. They run rather than hop, and a few species, such as the tree pipit, have the same tail-pumping habit that is characteristic of wagtails. Some pipits perch on rocks and trees.

Insect eaters

Pipits are insectivorous, eating mainly grasshoppers, ants, mosquitoes and beetles that live on the ground or among the grass. Snails, slugs, spiders and a few small seeds are also eaten. Rock pipits feed on winkles and the remains of fish which they find along the shore.

Nests are built in depressions in the ground where they are often completely hidden by grass. The favourite nesting sites are in the sides of banks, cliffs and cuttings. Grasses, bents, seaweed and similar material are woven into a cup among grass and herbage. The 3—7 eggs are incubated by the female for about 2 weeks. The male stays nearby, feeding the female and helping to feed the chicks, which leave the nest after just over a fortnight. Two broods are raised in one season.

Parallel evolution

The longclaws of Africa bear an amazing resemblance to the American meadowlarks —not true larks but relatives of mockingbirds and grackles. They are similar in appearance, and in habits. Their songs are similar and their nests are constructed in the same way. Furthermore, when approached they both turn away to hide their colourful underparts. This is a remarkable example of parallel evolution, in which two unrelated animals have evolved similar features and similar ways of life in response to the same type of environment.

Parallel evolution takes place when the two animals are separated geographically. If they lived in the same place they would compete for food and space. Conversely when two animals with very similar habits do live side by side, they are usually separated by the barriers of slightly differing habits, such as mating or feeding, or preferences for slightly different habitats. For example, one animal may prefer wet ground, the other dry ground. Such differences, perhaps trivial to us, are sufficient to prevent interbreeding. Many species of deermice (p 623) live in similar habitats but do not interbreed. They are very difficult to tell apart and very similar species with slightly different habits are called sibling species. The meadow pipit and tree pipit are sibling species; they are superficially similar and breed in the same places, but in slightly different habitats. The tree pipit, for instance, starts its song flight from a tree, the meadow pipit from the ground.

class	**Aves**
order	**Passeriformes**
family	**Motacillidae**

to be dangerous to humans. All are
members of the genus **Serrasalmus,**
having a general similarity of appearance
and habits. Some scientists, however,
classify them differently. Most of the
species average 8 in. in length but
Serrasalmus piraya, of the River São
Francisco in eastern Brazil, one of the
most dangerous, may reach 2 ft. Most of
them are olive-green or blue-black above
and silvery or dark grey on flanks and
belly. Some species have reddish or
yellowish tinted fins. The colours seem to
vary considerably from place to place and

ravel in South and
fail to contain some
piranha or piraya, the
ly very ferocious
the rivers of this region.
abounds in such vast
a serious pest, making
ns either very hazardous
e for fording or bathing.
nha applies loosely to
of which only 4 seem

△ *The gates of hell? A piran*
deadly teeth beneath its flaring

with age. For example, old
the white piranha **Serrasa**
found in the Amazon syste
eastern South America, are
enough to be called black p
  The body of the piranha i
and rather compressed fro
A large bony crest on top o
supports a keel on the back
keel on the belly is strength
row of enlarged scales bear

backwardly-directed points, so the deep and heavy forepart of the fish is provided with a cut-water above and below. There is a fleshy adipose fin on the back between the dorsal and tail fins. The tail is slender and muscular and together with the broad, tough, blade-like tail fin helps to drive the body through the water with great force. As in all really swift fish the scales are very small. The most striking feature is the mouth. The massive lower jaw has relatively huge muscles operating it. The teeth are large, flat and triangular with very sharp points. These points merely pierce the skin, the rest is done by the edges, which are literally razor-sharp. The teeth of the upper jaw are similar but much smaller and fit exactly into the spaces between the points of the lower ones when the mouth is closed. The jaws are so strong and the teeth so sharp that they can chop out a piece of flesh as neatly as a razor. The fact that there is a reliable record of a 100lb capybara reduced to a skeleton in less than a minute shows the efficiency of the teeth.

A few of the smaller species are kept in aquaria, the most popular seen in tropical fish stores and public aquaria being **Serrasalmus nattereri,** the red or common piranha, up to 1 ft long and coloured red on the underside and fins.

Some piranhas are found only in certain river systems, such as the Rio São Francisco, Rio Paraguay or Rio Orinoco, while others range over a wider area.

◁ Piranhas take their pickings and leave. They hunt in shoals of up to several thousand so they often make short work of a carcase.

Water alive with fish

Piranha hunt in shoals, sometimes of several thousands, so in places the water seems to be alive with them. Smaller fishes form their staple diet, but any animal entering or falling into the water accidentally may be attacked. They often attack each other. It is said that they will instantly be attracted by blood in the water but apparently anything out of the ordinary will attract them.

Waterplant hatcheries

It is thought that piranha breed when the rainy season sets in about January or February. The female deposits her eggs on water plants or roots. On hatching, the fry stay attached to the vegetation in clusters until they have absorbed most of the yolk sac, and then become free-swimming. *Serrasalmus spilopleura* is one of the few species which has been seen breeding in an aquarium. The female deposited her eggs carefully on aquatic plants, which is unlike the usual erratic spawning behaviour of most of the other members of its family. The male guards the eggs as well as the fry, when they hatch. These became free-swimming about 5 days after hatching.

Ferocity exaggerated?

The ferocity of the piranha has become almost legendary. Stories are told of a cow or a pig, falling into a river, being stripped to a skeleton in a few minutes. One of the most famous stories is that of a man, fording a stream on horseback, who was brought down and killed by a swarm of piranha. Later the bones of horse and rider were found, picked perfectly clean, the man's clothes undamaged. It is probable that a lot of the stories have been exaggerated. Some travellers now say that they have waded in or swam in rivers infested with piranha shoals and have never been attacked.

Marcel Cognac

Yet others say they have come on villages where hardly a native had not suffered the loss of a toe or finger. It is difficult to know what to believe but there must be some truth in the danger from these fish.

It is possible that the ferocity of the piranha may vary with the species and from place to place, and it may be that they are much more aggressive at the beginning of the rainy season when the males are guarding the eggs. This could also explain why it is that they will attack bathers at certain places in a river, where perhaps they have laid eggs, leaving others unmolested not far away. Nevertheless, those aquarists who keep these fishes admit to treating them with respect and taking extra care in feeding them, or when netting them to transfer them from one aquarium to another.

△ *No table manners. Piranhas have pointed teeth with razor-sharp edges which bite out neat chunks of meat from their victim.*
▽ *Cleaned out. A carcase is left to the flies.*

class	**Pisces**
order	**Cypriniformes**
family	**Characidae**
genus & species	*Serrasalmus nattereri* red or Natterer's piranha *S. piraya* piraya *S. rhombeus* white or spotted piranha *S. spilopleura* common piranha others

FGH Allen

Pitta

Some of the pittas are among the most colourful birds in the world. The name pitta is a latinization of a native word meaning small bird. There are about 23 species, about the size of a thrush, with long legs, large feet and very short tails, giving them a very 'front heavy' appearance. They are also known as painted thrushes, ground thrushes and jewel thrushes because of their similarity to true thrushes. The plumage of pittas is immensely rich and varied, being made up of broad patches of colours including greens, reds, yellow and blues. The Indian, Bengal or blue-winged pitta is aptly known in India as the 'nine-coloured one'. It is about 7 in. long. The head is reddish-yellow with a thin black band over the top of the head and broad ones running through the eyes. The back and wings are mainly green, the rump and 'shoulders' pale blue. The chin and throat are white and the rest of the underparts reddish-yellow except for a scarlet patch under the tail. Perhaps the most beautiful pitta is Steere's pitta that lives in the mountain forests of the Philippines. It has a black head, white throat, sky blue, black, and scarlet underparts and a green and blue sheen on the back and wings.

Pittas live in forests, jungle or tropical scrub. Most live in southeast Asia, especially in the Malayan peninsula and archipelago, but some are found as far east as Japan and Australia, where the noisy pitta is known as the dragon bird because of its gaudy colours. There are also two species living in Africa.

Arthur Christiansen

Heard not seen

The brilliant colours of these birds are not noticed in the forests as they are secretive and shy and would be easily overlooked if it were not for their calls. These are loud two or three note whistles, trills or grunts. When one pitta calls, others answer it; the Indian pitta sets up choruses of whistlings particularly at sunrise, and it is known in Ceylon as the '6-o'clock bird'.

Pittas spend most of the time on the forest floor hopping on their strong legs but they also ascend into the trees to sing and roost. Some flick their tails continuously like a moorhen. Some pittas are migratory. The Indian pitta moves into Ceylon for the breeding season while those breeding in temperate regions such as Japan and Australia migrate to the tropics. The African pitta breeds from central Tanzania to South Africa but moves northwards in winter to Uganda. The tropical pittas have no migrations but probably move about in search of fresh feeding grounds.

◁ *Banded pitta,* **Pitta guajana.** △ *Green-breasted pitta. Pittas tend to keep their feet on the ground, hopping around on their strong legs.*

Ground feeders

Pittas forage very much like thrushes; they examine the ground with their heads cocked to one side hopping forward to stab at an animal or to flick leaves aside and pick anything that is disturbed. They feed on small animals that live on the ground. Including earthworms, termites, beetles, centipedes and small lizards. Also like thrushes, noisy pittas feed on snails, carrying them to small stones or logs to smash open their shells.

Pugnacious pittas

Pittas lead solitary lives, not tolerating any other pittas in their territories, and becoming very aggressive during the breeding season. It is possible to lure the Indian pitta to within 20 ft by imitating its whistle. Some pittas, such as the African pitta, have a short display flight. They leap up from their perch

onto a branch, then fly in a small circle back to the perch. The flight is accompanied by a buzzing noise which is probably made by the wings. When the Indian pitta sees a rival it flashes its' wings and tail, showing off its brilliant colours, especially the white patches on the wings that are normally hidden when it is perched on a branch.

They breed when food is most abundant, from February to April in tropical Asia, from November to February in Africa and Australia, and May to August in the northern part of the pittas' range. The nest is an oval domed mass of twigs and leaves. The entrance is in the side and leads along a short tunnel to the nest chamber which is lined with leaves and rootlets. The nest is usually in a bush near the ground but may be as high as 30 ft up a tree. The eggs are round and glossy, and in India and Malaya a clutch of usually 3 or 4 eggs is laid, with fewer in Australia and South Africa. Both parents take part in incubating the eggs and feeding the young.

Discriminating pitta

In general, the small birds of tropical Asia have not been well studied, but one green-breasted pitta received more than its share of attention from Tom Harrisson, who has contributed so much to our knowledge of the wildlife of Malaysia. This pitta was kept in an aviary, where it became quite tame, while its food preferences were studied. It had a voracious appetite, eating more than its own weight of food every day. Its favourite food was earthworms followed by caterpillars provided that they were not hairy, cockroaches and small grasshoppers. Other animals formed second choice, and were eaten only when the favourites had been consumed. These included spiders, large wasps and large snails. Surprisingly a 3in. beetle and a 6in. centipede were completely consumed.

Observations such as these on the tastes of captive animals are instructive, especially when it is difficult to watch them feeding in

△ *Proud snail smasher. The handsome* **Pitta versicolor** *feeds mainly on land snails.*

the wild. It is particularly interesting to find why certain animals are not eaten by them, because they are too hard, too fast or poisonous, for instance. Even better, it is interesting to find that such animals as the centipede are eaten by the pitta. Experiments like this can be made on almost all pets, but it is worth remembering that individual animals, like people, have their fads, irrational though they may be.

class	**Aves**
order	**Passeriformes**
family	**Pittidae**
genus & species	*Pitta angolensis* *African pitta* *P. brachyura* *Indian pitta* *P. sordida* *green-breasted pitta* *P. steerei* *Steere's pitta* *P. versicolor* *noisy pitta*

Pit viper

Some of the most-feared snakes are to be found among the 60 species of pit vipers (family Crotalidae) including well known forms like the fer-de-lance, which has already been dealt with (p 748) and the sidewinder and the rattlesnakes, which we shall come to later. Here we shall consider others, such as the American water moccasin, copperhead and bushmaster, as well as the Asiatic pit vipers.

Pit vipers are a diverse group with several interesting specializations, which is why we have given them three entries. Here, while dealing with the family in general terms, we pay special attention to what has been called their sixth sense, the two pits on the head that give them their name.

Pit vipers are solenoglyph (see night adder, p 1568). That is, they have fangs which fold back and are erected when about to be used. Most are land-living, some are tree-dwellers, a few have taken to water and others lead a partially burrowing life. Water moccasins are heavy-bodied, up to 5 ft long, and while living on land they readily take to water when disturbed and they hunt in water. They are slate black to olive or tan with indistinct brown bands. The copperhead, a brown snake with hourglass markings along the back, is up to 3 ft long. It lives in rocky outcrops and quarries and among piles of rotting logs. The bushmaster is the longest of the American pit vipers, up to 12 ft, mainly grey and brown with large diamond blotches along the back. It has large venom glands and unusually long fangs. Its generic name **Lachesis** *is from one of the Fates that influenced the length of life of people — a grim pun by the scientist who named it, for the bushmaster is one of the most dangerous of snakes. The Asiatic pit vipers are of two kinds, tree-dwelling and ground-living, the first having prehensile tails that assist their climbing. The Himalayan pit viper lives at altitudes of 7 000 – 16 000 ft, sometimes being found even at the foot of glaciers.*

The Asiatic pit vipers are found mainly in eastern and southeast Asia with one species extending as far west as the mouth of the River Volga. Wagler's pit viper is kept in large numbers in the Snake Temple in Penang. The water moccasin and the copperhead are widespread over the eastern and middle United States, the bushmaster ranges from Costa Rica and Panama to northern South America.

Warmblooded food

The warning posture of the water moccasin, mouth open showing its white lining, gives it the alternative name of cottonmouth. It also vibrates its tail at the same time, like its relatives the rattlesnakes, although it has no rattle to make a warning sound. Pit vipers, apart from their pits, are very

△ *Head first:* Trimeresurus gramineus.
▷ *Overleaf: Pit viper* Bothrops schlegeli.

ordinary snakes. Some take a wide range of foods, like the water moccasin which eats rabbits, muskrats, ducks, fish, frogs, other snakes, birds' eggs, and nestlings. The copperhead eats small rodents, especially the woodmouse, other snakes, frogs, toads, and insects, including caterpillars and cicadas. The bushmaster, by contrast, takes mainly mammals, and pit vipers generally tend to hunt warm-blooded animals more than cold-blooded, as one would expect from snakes with heat-detector pits. They have one on each side of the head between the eye and the nostril. Using these a pit viper can pick up the trail of a warm-blooded animal.

'Seeing' heat

Each pit is $\frac{1}{8}$ in. across and $\frac{1}{4}$ in. deep. A thin membrane is stretched near the bottom and temperature receptors, 500 – 1 500 per sq mm, are packed within this membrane. These receptors are so sensitive they can respond to changes as small as 0·002 of a C°, and they allow a snake to locate objects 0·1 of a C° warmer or cooler than the surroundings. In more understandable terms a pit viper could detect the warmth of the human hand held a foot from its head. The membrane with its receptors can be compared to an eye with its retina. The overhanging lip of the pit casts 'heat shadows' onto it, so the snake is aware of direction, and since the 'fields of view' of the two pits overlap there is the equivalent of stereoscopic vision, giving a rangefinder. A pit viper hunting by day has the advantage of being able to follow an animal's heat trail through low vegetation after the animal has passed out of sight. It could, of course, do this equally well by scent. The facial pits come into their own in night hunting, when prey can be tracked by scent with the facial pits guiding the final strike. At first it was thought they had something to do with an accessory aid to smell or as an organ of hearing — snakes have no ears. Another suggestion was that they might be organs for picking up low-frequency air vibrations. Then, as late as 1892, it was noticed that a rattlesnake, one

of the pit vipers, was attracted to a lighted match. Then came the discovery that pythons have pits on their lips that are sensitive to heat. The first experiments on pit vipers were made in 1937, and left no doubt that the pits are heat detectors and further studies since have shown just how delicate they are.

Snakes in cold climates

Pit vipers usually bear living young. There are a few exceptions, the bushmaster being one, and that lives in the tropics. Pit vipers extend from the Volga across Asia and across America. There may be a direct connection between these two things. One of the advantages of bearing living young, as against laying eggs, is that the offspring are protected not only against enemies but also against low temperatures until they are at an advanced stage of development. At some time pit vipers must have crossed the land bridge that used to exist where the Bering Straits are now. This is well north, and it would have been far easier for snakes able to bear live young to survive in these latitudes and so make the crossing. It probably explains also why the Himalayan pit viper can live so near glaciers, and why the most southerly of all snakes is a pit viper named *Bothrops ammodytoides*, living in the Santa Cruz province of Argentina.

class	**Reptilia**
order	**Squamata**
suborder	**Serpentes**
family	**Crotalidae**
genera & species	***Ancistrodon contortrix*** copperhead *A. himalayanus* Himalayan pit viper *A. piscivorus water moccasin* ***Trimeresurus wagleri*** *Wagler's pit viper*

Plaice

The plaice is one of the best known of the flatfishes and commercially the most important. It has a flattened body, with the dorsal fin extending from the head almost to the tailfin, and the anal fin from behind the gill cover to the same point. The brownish, upper, or right side is marked with red spots, each of which is surrounded with a white ring in the adult. These may be pale when the fish has been resting on whitish pebbles. The underside is pearly white but can be partially or wholly coloured, a condition known as ambicoloration. It may take the form of scattered brown or black spots or patches on the white undersurface. Alternatively, only the hindend may be completely coloured as on the upper surface, including the red spots. When the pigmentation extends along the whole underside the undersurface of the head is usually white, but in exceptional cases even this may be coloured. The mouth is twisted, with the lower, or blind, side more developed and armed with a greater number of teeth. The small scales are embedded in the skin and there are bony knobs between the eyes. Plaice can grow to almost 3 ft long, but the usual size is much less.

They range from Iceland and the White Sea, along the coasts of Scandinavia, south through the North Sea to the coasts of France and the western Mediterranean. Plaice are not identical throughout their range but are split into a number of races. They vary in area of distribution, time and site of spawning, and in their degree of pigmentation.

Living magic carpet

Plaice live on sandy, gravelly or muddy bottoms, slightly buried, swimming just off the bottom at intervals through the day and night. They are said to be demersal or bottom-living fishes. They swim with vertical undulations of the flattened body, like a living magic carpet, then, holding the body rigid, they glide down. On touching bottom they undulate the fins to disturb sand or mud, which then settles on the fins, disguising the outline of the body. In this position a plaice breathes with a suction-pump action of the gill-covers.

Young plaice seem to go into a state resembling hibernation in winter. They remain quiescent in shallow water, slightly buried in the sand. At the appropriate time they move from shallow to deeper water.

Chisel and grinder

The teeth in the jaws of a plaice are chisel-like, but the throat teeth are blunt crushers. The food is mainly small molluscs but other small bottom-living invertebrates, such as worms, are eaten. Plaice swim over the shore at high tide to feed on the cockle and mussel beds. They hunt by sight not raising the head much off the bottom, but shooting forward horizontally with great accuracy to take the prey. Very small molluscs are taken whole into the stomach. Larger ones are crushed by the throat teeth. They also bite off the siphons of molluscs or the heads of worms sticking out of tubes.

Prolific spawnings

There is little in their outward appearance to tell male from female, but at spawning time if they are held up to the light the female roe shows as a small dark triangle. The male roe is a curved rounded line. The males reach the spawning grounds first and are still there after the females have gone. Spawning time differs from one part of the sea to another. Off the east coast of Scotland it is from early January to May, with a peak in March. In the Clyde estuary, on the west coast of Scotland, it is from February to June. In the southern North Sea it is from October to March.

To spawn, two plaice swim about 2½ ft off the bottom, the female lying diagonally across the male, releasing a stream of eggs while he emits a stream of milt. Spawning lasts less than a minute, after which the two separate and return to the bottom. Each female lays 50–400 thousand eggs, the number depending, it seems, on the length

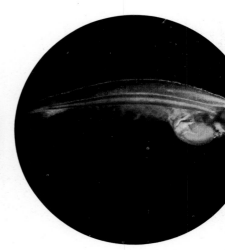

Plaice eggs with developing embryos.

of the fish. The transparent eggs, each in a tough capsule, are just under $\frac{1}{12}$ in. diameter. They float at or near the surface, and many are eaten before they can hatch, which they do in 8–21 days, according to the temperature of the water. The larvae are about ¼ in. long, without mouth or gills, and with the remains of a yolk sac attached which supplies them with food. This is the most vulnerable part of the life of a plaice. Apart from those eaten by other animals only 1 in every 100 thousand survive the first few weeks of larval life, or 2–5 for every pair of parent plaice. Although this seems disastrous the figures are put in perspective by the knowledge that in one area alone, half-way between the mouth of the Thames and the coast of Holland, 60 million plaice come together each year to spawn. The adults are probably protected by their colour and their habit of lying buried, but seals find them, and predatory fishes, such as cod, eat the small ones.

Plaice are of great economic value but of the tens of millions of plaice eaten each year in Europe, few are eaten at the right moment. Plaice has the best flavour when it is cooked immediately after being caught. The sole however, develops its characteristic taste 2–3 days after death due to the decomposition of the flesh with the formation of different chemical substances.

Baby food

As the contents of the yolk sac are being used up, the larval plaice starts to feed on diatoms. At this stage it has the normal fish larva shape, giving no indication of the adult shape to come. As it grows it graduates from small diatoms to larger diatoms then to larvae of small crustaceans, such as copepods, and molluscs. At this stage an important item is the planktonic food *Oikopleura*. After 2 months the larva gradually metamorphoses into a young flatfish, this takes about 2½ weeks. The body becomes flattened from side to side, the young plaice starts swimming on its side, the skull becomes twisted by growing more quickly on one side than the other, causing the left eye to be swung over to the right side. At the same time the young plaice leaves the upper waters for the seabed, settling on its left side, so its right side and both eyes are

Larva lives in plankton, off its yolk sac.

uppermost. As these changes have been taking place the young plaice (still only ½ in. long) has been carried by currents to its inshore nursery ground.

The account given above of the feeding of the larvae is only a generalization. The food taken varies in different places, the plaice taking whatever is available. In Scottish coastal waters they eat mainly worm larvae, crustacean eggs and larval molluscs. Off Plymouth, copepods and other small crustaceans are eaten, in the Irish Sea the larvae feed on small copepods, and spores of algae, and in southern North Sea it is mainly *Oikopleura*. The survival of the larvae can be seriously affected if supplies of these foods are low in a given area.

How they grow

After the ½in. young plaice has settled on the bottom it reaches 2¾ in. by the age of 1 year, 5 in. by 2 years, nearly 8 in. by 3 years, 10½ in. by 4 years and 13 in. by 5 years of age. These figures are for females, the males being smaller. On average, the males reach

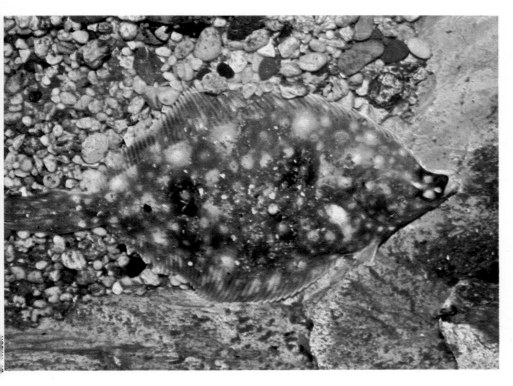

sexual maturity in 2—3 years, the females in 4—5 years. The figures must be read as approximations because average sizes of plaice have been found to vary: 17 in. in the North Sea, 15 in. in the English Channel, 13 in. in the Kattegat and 10 in. in the Baltic. These are, again, merely examples to show how size can vary, with environmental conditions. A 2ft plaice is 20 or more years old, and a 33in. plaice, which is one of the largest recorded, would be about 40 years old.

Plaice life history

Like many marine fishes the plaice lays a large number of eggs to offset heavy predation. The dramatic part of the life cycle occurs after 2 months in preparation for life on the seabed. The body becomes flattened from side to side; the skull is twisted by growing more quickly on one side than the other, causing the left eye to be swung over to the right side; then the young plaice settles with both eyes uppermost.

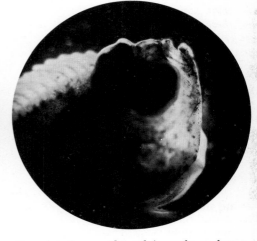

As yolk sac is used up the mouth develops.

Left eye migrates as larva swims on its side.

Eye migration complete, plaice settles on bottom.

◁ *Face to face with the adult plaice. With distorted mouth and transposed eye it now lives permanently at the bottom of the sea, lying on its left side.*

In this plaice the upper surface is mottled light grey to suit its background of shell-gravel. The plaice in the top picture has a brown mottling because it is lying on differently coloured sandy gravel. A plaice can change its colour and patterns to blend in with its background. A hormone is secreted which alters the shape of the pigment cells thus changing the colour of the plaice's body.

class	**Pisces**
order	**Pleuronectiformes**
family	**Pleuronectidae**
genus & species	***Pleuronectes platessa***

Plains-wanderer

These unusual, and now rare, Australian birds, also called collared hemipodes, share with their relatives, the buttonquails, and with painted snipe and phalaropes, the unusual feature of having dominant females. The female plains-wanderer is 5 in. long, 1 in. longer than the male, and has brighter plumage. The plumage is not gaudy but has intricate patterns of reddish-brown, buff and black. The wings are short and rounded. At one time the plains-wanderer was classified with the buttonquails (p 340) to which it is very similar in appearance, but it has certain structural differences; it has a hind toe, and pointed rather than oval eggs.

Plains-wanderers live in southeastern Australia, from Lake Frome in the west and as far north as central Queensland in the east. They seem to be most abundant in Victoria. They stick to the dry plains and grasslands, avoiding the scrub regions where the buttonquails live.

Reluctant fliers

Plains-wanderers are usually active at night and move about in pairs or family parties rather than in flocks like their relatives. They migrate in search of feeding grounds, flying with rapidly whirring wings. Usually, however, they are very unwilling to fly. If disturbed they run through the grass, occasionally rising on tiptoe to peer around, or freeze, crouching motionless, and it is sometimes possible to catch them by hand.

The food of the plains-wanderer is mainly seeds of grass and other low plants, together with some insects.

Paterfamilias

The breeding habits of the plains-wanderer have not been studied in detail, but it is known that the female takes an active part in courtship and that the male incubates the eggs and guards the chicks. Whether the female mates with several males, as in buttonquails, is not known.

The nest is a grass-lined depression usually sheltered by tall grass or a bush. There are four eggs to a clutch, pale yellow or green with grey spots. The incubation period is not known but the chicks leave the nest shortly after hatching.

Causes of decline

The plains-wanderer is one of the growing number of animals that is becoming rare or extinct before their habits have been studied. In recent times some birds have become extinct before their eggs and incubation periods have been described. At one time the plains-wanderer was quite common and even now it is not so rare as to be put on the endangered list, but since Europeans settled in Australia its life has become more and more precarious. The grasslands have been transformed by agriculture; even stock farming drives out the plains-wanderer because sheep eat the seed-bearing plants on which it lives. Introduced rabbits, and fires, have had the same effect, and those that survive fall prey to foxes and feral cats.

class	**Aves**
order	**Gruiformes**
family	**Pedionomidae**
genus & species	*Pedionomus torquatus*

Plains-wanderers: the female has an orange bib.

Platy

*This is a small tropical fish, a longstanding favourite with aquarists who shortened its scientific name **Platypoecilus** to platy. The scientific name has now been changed to **Xiphophorus** but platy still persists as the common name.*

The wild platy is a deep-bodied freshwater fish of Mexico and Guatemala with a single dorsal fin and a relatively large, rounded tail fin. The males are up to $1\frac{3}{4}$ in. long, the females up to $2\frac{1}{4}$ in. The colour is brownish to dark olive on the back, the flanks being bluish and the underside whitish. The fins are almost transparent but in the male the pectoral fins are bluish at the tips and the anal and tail fins have a greenish-white band. Platys have also been called moonfish, a name seldom used now, because of the mark at the base of the tail fin which looks like a crescent moon. This mark is, however, variable and is missing in many individuals, and the colours also are variable even in the wild forms, in which black checkered and red varieties are not uncommon.

*A second species, from another part of Mexico, was named **Platypoecilus variatus**, or the variable platy, because of the range of colours it shows. It is similar to the first species and some experts treat the two as a single species.*

Rainbow colours

Platys are sometimes described as cheerful and not at all shy, which is just what an aquarist likes in his pets. They are easy to keep and they breed well, often producing colour varieties that can be selected and which breed true. They have, in fact, provided more colour varieties than probably any other aquarium fishes. Among these are the blue platys, in a wide range of blues, the red platys which at first were red, stippled with the black dots of the wild platy but are now bred in a pure deep red form, and the black platy which is green or yellow with a broad black stripe along the body, or may be all black except for the fins. Then a European aquarist found a yellow variety among his stock which became known as the golden platy, and when this was crossed with the wild form it gave the wagtail platy, which had a grey body and black fins at first, but later developed a yellow body and black fins. By breeding platys the aquarist was able to amuse himself with producing new colour varieties or even to study heredity.

Casual courtship

As well as eating animals such as water fleas and mosquito and midge larvae, platys take plant food and are especially fond of nibbling the green algae that grow on the sides of an aquarium. Courtship and mating are very brief. As the colours of the male intensify he either swims alongside the female or dashes about encircling her with outspread fins. Then suddenly they mate, in one quick movement, while both partners are still moving forward. Fertilisation is internal and the babies are born alive, 10 – 75 at a time. The growth and general welfare of the young depends on the temperature of the water; for example they grow noticeably faster and survive better at 22°C/97°F than at 23°C/103°F.

In aquaria platys readily hybridize with the related swordtails, yet although these two fishes live almost side by side in their natural habitat they have not been known to hybridize there. Careful study of this suggests that courtship is not only a way of bringing the sexes into breeding condition, but is also a kind of language by which members of the species recognize each other and also learn to tell the difference between their own kind and members of another species. The courtship of the platys and swordtails is very similar differing only in a number of small details. None of these is important on its own but together they keep members of the different species apart. In an aquarium, where there is not the same wide choice of partners the 'language' breaks down and a male and a female of different species will come together and breed, giving rise to hybrids.

Cancer research

From one such hybridization came a significant discovery of medical importance. When a spotted platy was crossed with a green swordtail the offspring always developed cancerous growths along the sides of the body, remarkably like certain types of cancer in human beings. Here was an example of an heritable cancer—one that could be produced to order merely by crossing two kinds of fishes. This made it possible to study the genetics of cancer in a species that bred rapidly so giving quick results. Comparable studies on humans would prove long and difficult.

class	Pisces
order	Atheriniformes
family	Poeciliidae
genus & species	*Xiphophorus maculatus*

▽ *No colours barred. Through selective breeding platys have probably provided more colour varieties than any other aquarium fish.*

Michael Johns

Platypus

Today the platypus is accepted as an unusual animal of quaint appearance, but it is not difficult to imagine its impact on the scientific world when it was first discovered. So strange did the creature appear that one scientist named it **paradoxus,** and a paradox it was with duck-like bill, furry mammalian coat and webbed feet.

Known as the duckbill, watermole or duckmole, the platypus is one of Australia's two egg-laying mammals, the other being the spiny anteater. The platypus is about 2 ft long including a 6in. beaver-like tail and weighs about $4\frac{1}{2}$ lb, the males being slightly larger than the females. The 'bill' is a sensitive elongated snout and is soft, like doeskin, not horny as is popularly supposed.

Although bizarre in appearance, the platypus is well adapted to its semi-aquatic life. The legs are short with strong claws on the toes and the feet are webbed. The webbing on the forefeet extends well beyond the toes, but can be turned back when on land, leaving the claws free for walking and digging. The eye and the opening to the inner ear lie on each side of the head in a furrow which can be closed when the platypus submerges. There are no external ears, thus the platypus is blind and deaf when under water. Young have teeth, but these are replaced in the adult by horny ridges.

Thick loose skin makes the barrel-shaped body of the platypus appear larger than it is. The pelt consists of a dense woolly undercoat and long shiny guard hairs. The colour varies from sepia brown to almost black above and is silver, tinged with pink or yellow underneath; females can be identified by the more pronounced reddish tint of their fur. Adult males have hollow spurs, connected to venom glands, on the ankle of each hind limb. The poison from them can be quite harmful to a man, although not fatal.

The platypus was not discovered until 1796, nearly 200 years after the first wallaby, for instance, had been seen by a European. This is not as strange as might appear at first sight, for aquatic animals tend to be elusive particularly if, like the platypus, they are nocturnal.

Its range can be seen on the map. The western limits are the Leichhardt River in North Queensland, and the Murray, Onkaparinga and Glenelg rivers, just within the border of South Australia. It is found in all fresh water, from clear icy streams at 5 000 ft to lakes and warm coastal rivers.

▷ Platypus dives in a cloud of silvery bubbles. When underwater the platypus is blind and deaf so it relies mainly on its sense of touch, highly developed in the soft rubbery bill.

◁ Out of its front door and into the river.

Australian News & Information Bureau

Hearty appetite

Like many small energetic animals the platypus has a voracious appetite, and probably needs more food, relative to its weight, than any other mammal. It feeds mainly in the early morning and late evening, on crayfish, worms and other small water animals. It probes for these with its bill and at the same time takes in mud and sand, which are apparently necessary for breaking up the food. During the day the platypus rests in burrows dug out of the banks, coming out at night to forage for food in the mud of the river-bottom.

Egg-laying mammal

The breeding season is from August to November and mating takes place in the water, after an elaborate and unusual courtship. Among other manoeuvres, the male will grasp the female's tail and the two will then swim slowly in circles. The female digs a winding, intricate burrow in a bank 25—35 ft, sometimes as much as 60 ft, long, 12—15 in. below the surface of the ground. At the end, a nesting chamber is excavated and lined with wet grass and leaves. The female carries these by wrapping her tail around a bundle. Usually two soft-shelled white eggs are laid, each $\frac{1}{2}$ in. diameter. They often stick together, which prevents them rolling, and the wet leaves and grass keep them from drying out. Before retiring to lay her eggs, 2 weeks after mating, the female blocks the tunnel at intervals with earth, up to 8 in. thick, which she tamps into position with her tail. During the incubation period of 7—10 days she rarely leaves the nest but each time she does so these earth blocks are rebuilt. Presumably this is a defensive measure, but in fact today the platypus has virtually no natural enemies, although a carpet-snake or goanna may occasionally catch one. The inference is that in past ages natural enemies did exist in some numbers and the earth-block defences were very necessary. This is an example of what is known as 'fossil behaviour' and the platypus itself is a living fossil.

△ *In the water the platypus uses its strong webbed forefeet for swimming and its hind legs as rudders. On land its forefeet are used for digging and to press the water out of its fur before it enters its burrow.*

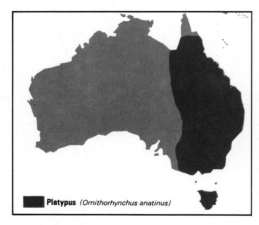

Platypus *(Ornithorhynchus anatinus)*

Use for spilt milk

The young platypus is naked and blind, and its eyes do not open for 11 weeks. It is weaned when nearly 4 months old, at which age it takes to the water. The mother has no teats; milk merely oozes through slits on her abdomen where it is licked up by the babies. A platypus matures at about $2\frac{1}{2}$ years and has a life span of 10 years or more.

Competing with rabbits

Formerly hunted ruthlessly for its beaver-like pelt, the platypus is now rigidly protected. Too often, however, it falls foul of wire cages set under water for fish. Should the platypus enter one it cannot escape and will drown, as it is not able to stay under water for much more than 5 minutes. The introduced rabbit of Australia threatens the platypus in a different way. Where rabbits have driven too many tunnels the platypus cannot breed: it needs undisturbed soil for its breeding burrows. Fortunately, although reduced in numbers, it is now well protected by the Australian authorities and it is in no danger of extinction.

Creature of contrast

Fortunately for the sanity of naturalists, the paradoxical facts that the platypus, a mammal, laid eggs and suckled its young were not known when it was first discovered. In 1884, WH Caldwell, who had gone to Australia specially to study the platypus, dissected a female which had already laid one egg and was ready to lay another. Thrilled by this discovery he electrified members of the British Association for the Advancement of Science, then meeting in Montreal, with his laconic telegram—'Monotremes oviparus, ovum meroblastic' (monotremes egg-laying, egg only partially divides). Delegates stood and cheered, for controversy over this point had raged in the scientific world for some years.

Long before this, in 1799, the first dried skin reached London and came into the hands of Dr Shaw, then assistant-keeper in the Natural History section of the British Museum. When Dr Shaw saw the skin he literally could not believe what he saw. At that time visitors to the Far East were bringing back fakes such as the 'eastern-mermaid', made from the skin of a monkey skilfully sewn to the tail of a fish. It is not surprising, therefore, that Dr Shaw should suspect someone had grafted the bill of a duck on to the body of a quadruped. He tried to prise off the bill, and today the marks of his scissors can still be seen on the original skin which is preserved in the British Museum (Natural History).

class	**Mammalia**
order	**Monotremata**
family	**Ornithorhynchidae**
genus & species	***Ornithorhynchus anatinus***

Plover

These pretty waders which can often be seen running rapidly along the foreshore, stopping for a moment and then running, are part of the large family of waders which includes the lapwings, dotterel and killdeer that have been treated separately. Attention is given here to the golden plovers **Pluvialis** and sand plovers **Charadrius.**

The four species of golden plover are distinguished by spangled black and gold backs. Their underparts are usually black in the breeding season. At this time, the male golden plover, about 11 in. long, is spangled above and black below, with a white line separating the two that runs from above the base of the bill, over the eye and follows the margin of the wing. The female is very similar. In winter the black disappears and the underparts become white with some mottling. The golden plover lives in Iceland, Faeroes, the British Isles, parts of northern Europe and northeastern Siberia. The closely related American golden plover is smaller, 9½ in. long, but otherwise is similar to the European golden plover. It breeds in the Arctic regions of Canada, Alaska and Siberia. The grey plover, known in North America as the black-bellied plover, also breeds in the Arctic, but not in Greenland or Scandinavia. The breeding plumage of the male is silver, rather than gold-spangled. The fourth species is the so-called dotterel of New Zealand which has reddish-brown underparts.

The sand plovers are smaller, generally brown or grey above and white underneath with black bands across the breast and face. They include the ringed plover of northern Europe, together with the British Isles, northern Asia, Greenland, Iceland, Spitzbergen and parts of Arctic Canada. The little ringed plover is found over most of Europe, North Africa and Asia as far as Japan and New Guinea. The Kentish or snowy plover breeds in North America, the West Indies, Europe, many parts of Africa, Asia and Australia. It no longer breeds in Kent or anywhere else in the British Isles. The most unusual of the plovers is the wrybill of New Zealand. It is the only bird with a bill that is bent sideways.

Spangled male golden plover struts jauntily along in his attractive breeding plumage—a striking white line separates spangled top from black below.

Eric Hosking

Long migrations

Many plovers make long migrations to and from breeding grounds. One of the less spectacular is that of the wrybill, which breeds in South Island, New Zealand and winters in North Island. The American golden plover, however, travels from the high Arctic to Argentina and Australia and the grey plover, another Arctic breeder, winters in Chile, South Africa and Australia.

Plovers live on shores or very open country, usually near water, although the mountain plover of the dry plains of the southwest United States never lives near water. Outside the breeding season they gather in flocks to feed in estuaries, flying together with the precision often seen in flocks of waders.

More than it can chew

Plovers eat mainly small animals such as insects, worms and small molluscs. Occasionally one tries to tackle too much, for ringed plovers and others have been found caught with their bills between the shells of cockles. The wrybill uses its odd bill for probing under stones in search of insects. On migration the American golden plover eats large numbers of grasshoppers and locusts. Berries are also eaten, especially by the American golden plover. It lives on the previous year's berries when it arrives in the Arctic during spring, before the insects have appeared.

Careful guardians

Plovers' nests are usually no more than scrapes in the ground, without any lining. Many species regularly lay a clutch of 4 eggs but there may be as few as 2, as in the wrybill, or as many as 5. Both parents incubate and tend the young, who leave the nest shortly after hatching. The incubating period is about 4 weeks in larger species and 3 weeks in smaller species. The chicks fly in 3–5 weeks.

Plovers are very inconspicuous when not in a flock and can often be found only by searching for the source of their whistling calls. The nests are also very difficult to find

Cockle shell nesting site: a Kentish plover about to settle on its mottled clutch.

and plovers regularly attempt to divert intruders by distraction displays in which they make themselves conspicuous. One display is the 'broken wing' in which one wing droops, showing up the white plumage underneath. In the 'rodent run' the plover runs with its tail drooping. The ringed plover, moreover, spreads its tail to show a conspicuous white border as it runs away from an intruder.

More about migrations

Usually if one is studying a bird's migration it is possible to go to one place to watch the movement both to and from the breeding grounds. If, however, one watched the American golden plover flying down through Labrador or New England it would

be no use coming back to see them return in the autumn, for they return by a different route. The golden plovers travel south from Arctic Canada and Alaska across Hudson's Bay to Newfoundland and New England, then across the sea to South America. In spring they return through Central America and up the interior of North America. There is a reason for this circular tour; the plovers are taking the shortest route that allows adequate food on the way. In the autumn they travel to the Atlantic coast to gorge on berries before setting off on their long sea journey to South America. The return trip would be impossible in spring because this area would still be foggy and frost-bound, offering no comfort to the plovers after a non-stop ocean flight. The interior of the continent however, warms up quickly in spring and food will already be available.

Another interesting migration is made by the ringed plover. It has recently colonised Greenland, Ellesmere Island and Baffin Island. These populations do not migrate to South America, but cross to Iceland then follow their ancestors' trail down through Britain into Europe and West Africa.

class	**Aves**
order	**Charadriiformes**
family	**Charadriidae**
genera & species	***Anarhynchus frontalis*** *wrybill* ***Charadrius alexandrinus*** *Kentish plover* ***C. dubius*** *little ringed plover* ***C. hiaticula*** *ringed plover* ***C. montanus*** *mountain plover* ***Pluvialis apricaria*** *golden plover* ***P. dominica*** *American golden plover* ***P. squatarola*** *grey plover* ***P. obscurus*** *New Zealand dotterel, others*

◁ *Overleaf: Flock of grey plovers take to flight.*
▽ *Distraction: a Kentish plover feigns a broken wing in an attempt to divert the photographer's attention from a well-camouflaged nest.*

We-Ha

*Fan dance: a long legged plume moth **Pterophorus pentadactylus** looks rather ghost-like with its 'feathered' wings spread out at right angles to its body.*

Plume moth

*The plume moths make up a comparatively small family whose wings are divided into 'feathers'. The forewings which are very long are divided into two or three parts and the hindwings into three or four parts. A few have wings without clefts, such as the European genus **Agdistis**. The bodies of plume moths are very long and slender, as are the legs which have prominent spurs. The wingspan ranges from $\frac{1}{4}-2$ in. The flight is feeble and with their long body and legs, plume moths look rather like daddy-long-legs (p 601). When at rest the forewings are rolled around the hindwings and usually held straight out at right angles to the body.*

There are about 600 species of plume moths, found in most parts of the world. Closely related are the feather-winged moths of the family Orneodidae, most of which are found in Asia. The many-plume moth, with $\frac{1}{2}$ in. wingspan, is found in Europe and the temperate parts of North America. The fore- and hindwings are divided into six and look like a pair of feather fans.

A watery death

During the day a sudden glimpse may be caught of a disturbed plume moth as it flies out of a plant in which it has been resting. Usually plume moths are active only in the evening or at night. They make themselves very inconspicuous when at rest among the herbage or hedgerows. Adults of *Agdistis* hold their rolled wings pointing forward in a line with the body, so they resemble the dried grass on which they rest. This camouflage is improved by their blackish markings which look like moulds.

Plume moths live on a variety of food plants but are only occasionally pests. The grape vine plume of the United States attacks the sprouting leaves of vines but is not as serious a pest as *Exelastis atomosa* of India which burrows into pods and eats the growing peas. The pupa is later formed within the pod. The leaves and sometimes the flowers of a plant are the usual food of plume moth caterpillars. The caterpillars bore into the leaf and flower stems making them wither, or they bind the leaves into a rosette with silk strands so they are protected while they eat. The caterpillars of *Stenoptilia pneumonanthes*, which feed on marsh gentians, are sometimes drowned by rain when they feed in the cup-shaped flowers. The caterpillars of *Agdistis bennetii* are liable to suffer the same fate. They feed and hibernate on the leaves of sea lavender, where they are in danger of being inundated by high tides.

Mobile pupae

Eggs of plume moths are usually laid on the leaves of the food plants and the caterpillars feed on these leaves or flowers, or bore into the stems and buds. There are often two generations in one year, the second hibernating as caterpillars in stems of the food plants. The pupa is soft and hairy and hangs from a leaf or stem like the chrysalises of some butterflies. Some species weave a cocoon that is no more than a few strands of silk thrown around the body. The caterpillars of the triangle plume, which has black triangles on its forewings, hatch in June and feed on coltsfoot. The adults emerge and are on the wing from August to September then a second generation of caterpillars becomes active in September. They feed on the leaves of coltsfoot, before burrowing into the stems to hibernate. In the spring they feed on buds and flowers then pupate in the seed heads, binding the seeds with silk so they do not fall. The adults emerge in May.

The pupa of *Leioptilus lienigianus* jerks sharply if disturbed, perhaps startling a predator. That of *Platyptilia calodactyla* is also mobile. It often wriggles to the surface of its burrow in a leaf but retreats if disturbed. It is prevented from emerging too far by an anchor rope of silk attached to its hind end and the inside of the burrow.

Preying on the predator

Adults of *Trichoptilus paludum* can sometimes be seen during the day, flying over boggy heaths and moors. They lay their eggs on sundew, a peculiar bog plant that captures and devours insects. This habit is found in other bog plants and is probably related to the deficiency of nitrate in boggy soils. The deficiency is made up by breaking down protein in the insects' bodies. The upper surfaces of sundew leaves bear hairs surmounted by glands. When an insect lands on a leaf it is trapped in sticky secretions, the hairs of the plant bend towards it and secrete fluids that digest it. The products of digestion are then absorbed by the plant. The caterpillars of *Trichoptilus* feed on sundew leaves, and presumably in some way avoid being caught and digested, but it seems to be as precarious a way of life as living on man-eating tigers.

phylum	**Arthropoda**
class	**Insecta**
order	**Lepidoptera**
family	**Pterophoridae**
genera & species	**Orneodes hexadactyla** *many-plume moth* **Oxyptilus periscelidactylus** *grapevine plume moth* **Platyptilia gonodactyla** *triangle plume moth, others*

Pochard

Pochards dive for their food, like grebes, with a quick jump up before plunging under. Thus they are more adapted to an aquatic life than their dabbling relatives, the mallard and pintail. Their legs are placed well back on the body and most pochards have difficulty in walking. They come ashore mainly for roosting and nesting. The short, heavy body has a large head and long neck. The males have an eclipse plumage when they live in the temperate zone. The three pochards in the genus **Netta** are less adapted to an aquatic life and do not dive as well as the other species. They float higher in the water and walk more easily. The other 11 pochards are classed in the genus **Aythya**, of which there are four groups. The first of these includes the European pochard and the American canvasback and redhead. These are similar in plumage and important game birds. The second group is made up of pochards called white-eyes; the third group of pochards are mostly black and white, including the tufted duck and New Zealand scaup. The fourth group includes the tree scaups.

The most important pochard is the canvasback that breeds in western North America from Alaska to New Mexico and migrates down the flyways (see pintail p 1769) as far as South America. Even if it is not the most shot-at of ducks it is the most esteemed for eating. Most of the body

△ Famous North American sporting duck, the canvasback, identified by reddish brown head.
▷ European tufted duck—the black and white male seen here has a thin drooping crest; the female is browner and has a rudimentary crest.
▽ Rosybill, **Netta peposaca**, like the other two of its genus, is a non-diving pochard.

is light grey with black on the breast, and a russet head and neck. A closely related pochard is 18 in. long and breeds in Europe and central Asia. The plumage of the two species is almost identical. Next in importance to these two is the redhead or American pochard. The tufted duck, 17 in. long, is an Old World bird, ranging from Iceland to Kamchatka. It is all black with very distinctive white flanks and a small trailing crest. The scaup duck, with a circumpolar Arctic distribution, has a plumage similar to the tufted ducks, but lacks the tuft and has a light grey back.

Most pochards live in the northern hemisphere but in the south there are the southern pochard from Abyssinia to South Africa, the New Zealand scaup and the Australian white-eye, which colonised New Zealand but later died out.

Commuting to feed

Pochards migrate in V-formation; some times the whole flock plunges spectacularly from a great height towards a sheet of water Their habits are in general similar to thos of dabbling ducks. Pochards breed in fresh water and some spend the winter in sal water or the brackish water of estuarie where they can be found in large flocks Others only go to sea during very col weather. There may be an excess of male in the flocks, as much as 50 to 1. They feed mainly in the morning and evening and sometimes at night. Shallower waters are preferred for feeding and in the evening there is a 'flight' from larger, and safer waters to smaller pools. Pochards are awkward when they take off or land, as the have to run over the water before gainin sufficient lift with their short wings.

Tasty duck and celery

Pochards feed on aquatic plants and animals, usually diving to collect them from the bottom. The canvasback eats mainly plant food and for this reason its flesh tastes better than that of the European pochard which eats mainly small animals such as insects, molluscs, worms, small frogs and a few fish. About three-quarters of the canvasback's food is vegetable including water-lilies and wild oats. The best tasting canvasbacks are those that have fed on the 'wild celery' that grows around Chesapeake Bay. This has long ribbonlike leaves and grows just offshore in great quantities. The canvasbacks prefer the roots which taste like garden celery. They dive to uproot the plants and bite off the roots, leaving the rest to float away. Redhead and scaup also dive for water celery roots, but other ducks, such as the baldpate or American wigeon *Mareca americana*, and coots, wait for the canvasbacks to surface with a bill full of roots and then steal it from them.

Some pochards swim underwater with their wings, staying under for $\frac{1}{2}-1$ minute or more. European pochards and tufted ducks prefer to feed in shallow water 2—6 ft deep, but scaups, will feed in deep water.

Cuckoo duck

Pochards nest in marshes or lakes and ponds where there is abundant cover around the edges. Nests are often quite close together and are usually very near water. Canvasbacks and European pochards may nest among reeds in the water, raising the nest above the water level with a pile of dead reeds and other plants. The redhead sometimes lays its eggs in the nest of another duck, cuckoo-like, and the young are raised by foster parents. The female broods the 6—12 eggs, rarely leaving the nest for the 23—26 day period. The male usually leaves her before the chicks are hatched, although the male scaup sometimes stays with his family. The chicks are led from the nest as

Red-crested pochard nest. The nest is covered by the parents, hiding the eggs from predators and conserving some heat. This behaviour is seen in most ducks and some grebe species.

soon as they are dry, and guarded and fed by the female, who brings food to the surface for them before they have learnt to dive. The canvasback abandons her brood early, and these broods band together, forming groups of first year ducks.

Making ducks precocious

The study of an animal's behaviour is often made by presenting a test animal with the different situations that it would normally meet when diving, feeding, courting, fighting and so on. From this the stimuli eliciting various forms of behaviour can be determined. A well-known example of this is the male robin attacking a bunch of red feathers, from which we learn that it is by the red

breast that a robin recognises a rival. But the response to stimuli often varies and depends on other factors, such as the internal state of the animal. It has been found that some behaviour is controlled by hormones within the body (see phalarope p 1741). When the testes and ovaries are not functioning sexual and aggressive behaviour are usually absent. Such behaviour can be stimulated by the injection of sex hormones and it has been found that the chicks of many birds may perform courtship displays when treated with these hormones. The male downy chicks of redheads start to perform courtship displays and calls after treatment with testosterone, the male sex hormone, as do male chicks of mallard and pintails. The displays given are, however, only those that appear in the adult 'spontaneously'. That is, they may be given when the male is not specifically courting. The treated chicks did not give displays that required the presence of a mate. This shows that courtship displays, like other forms of behaviour, are sometimes dependent only on the state of the animal, but at other times the animal also needs external signs or stimuli to trigger off the behaviour.

class	**Aves**
order	**Anseriformes**
family	**Anatidae**
genera & species	*Aythya americana* redhead *A. australis* Australian white-eye *A. ferina* European pochard *A. fuligula* tufted duck *A. marila* scaup *A. novae-zeelandiae* New Zealand scaup *A. valisineria* canvasback *Netta erythopthalma* southern pochard, others

Armada fleet of scaup ducklings tended by a female. The breeding grounds of this hardy duck are often within the Arctic circle.

Pocket gopher

The name of these small hamster-like animals is derived from the two external furlined cheek pouches, which run from face to shoulder. They are used for carrying food and are turned inside out when they need cleaning (see pocket mouse p 1802).

There are 30 species of pocket gophers which vary considerably in size, with a body length from 3½ to 13 in. and tails from 1½ to 5½ in. The coat is usually thick and smooth, lighter and thinner on the underside. Pocket gophers living in hot lowland areas have shorter coarser fur. The fur colour varies from almost black through all shades of brown to off-white. Albinos are not uncommon. **Macrogeomys** *and* **Zygogeomys** *have characteristic white patches.*

The body is adapted for burrowing. The skull is large and angular, the body thickset and tapering towards the tail. Ears and eyes are small, the latter being kept moist with a thick fluid to keep the

eyeball free from dirt. The legs are short and powerful, especially the forelegs, which have long digging claws. The tail is almost naked and is very sensitive to touch. By arching the tail to raise the tip just off the ground, a pocket gopher can feel its way as it moves rapidly backwards in its burrow.

All pocket gophers have long curving upper incisors, behind which the lips close to prevent earth entering the mouth while they are burrowing.

Peculiar to North America, pocket gophers are found from western Canada south to Panama. They do not travel far and are found in localised areas, often restricted to valleys by mountain barriers.

The solitary burrower

These solitary rodents spend almost their entire life underground, only very occasionally coming to the surface to collect food. Each gopher lives within its own system of burrows and they only come together at mating times. Young pocket gophers can sometimes be found above ground after leaving their parents, and in drought or

after floods adult pocket gophers may be driven out to look for new homes.

The individual burrows are often extensive and are marked by fan shaped mounds of earth around the entrances. These are carefully blocked with earth as protection against predators and to maintain suitable temperature and humidity. There are two types of tunnels: long, shallow ones, used mainly for getting food, and deep ones, used for shelter, with separate chambers for food storage, nesting and latrines. A great assortment of other animals use inhabited and abandoned gopher burrows.

Pocket gophers dig with their strong foreclaws, the curved incisors being used for loosening hard earth and rocks. The incisors are growing continually so replacing the worn surfaces. They may grow as much as 20 in. in one year.

Pocket gophers do not hibernate but may remain relatively inactive for long periods. Evidence of their winter activity is strikingly apparent when the snows melt in high pastures, revealing gopher burrows within the snow lined with earth, and left behind as a mass of criss-crossing 'cores' showing

that the animals have burrowed at several levels. The tunnels are up to 40 ft long and 2—3 in. diameter.

Underground vegetarian

The staple diet of pocket gophers is tubers, bulbs and roots of plants which can be found and eaten in the security of the burrow. Occasionally at night, or on overcast days, pocket gophers surface in search of food, but more often plants are seen disappearing in jerks as, from the safety of its burrow, a pocket gopher pulls them down. In agricultural regions, crops often suffer badly as gophers favour sweet-potatoes, sugar cane, peas and fruit. Gophers never seem to drink, probably getting enough moisture from their plant food.

Little is known about the breeding and courtship of gophers, but if the soil and food conditions are suitable their numbers increase rapidly. A female may have one or more litters a year and the number of off-spring varies considerably from 2 to 11. The newborn young, weighing about $\frac{1}{12}$ oz, are blind and almost hairless. In most species they leave their mother at about 2 months to make their own burrow network. They are sexually mature within 3 months.

Safe underground

The best protection a pocket gopher has against its enemies is its underground way of life, but in fights with its own kind it is protected by the loose skin and thick hair around the head. Predators, such as coyotes, badgers and skunks, sometimes succeed in digging pocket gophers out and if they have to come above ground for any length of time owls and hawks make short work of them. Athough snakes and weasels hunt pocket gophers down their burrows, man is by far their worst enemy.

Pocket gophers can be very destructive, eating crops, burrowing through dykes and contributing to soil erosion. But on the credit side they do sterling work improving the soil by loosening, aerating and mixing it with organic matter. They also conserve water since, after a heavy snowfall, the melted water sinks deep into the earth through the maze of gopher tunnels instead of flowing straight into the nearest stream.

All manner of snares, traps, sling shots and spears are used to eliminate the pocket gophers and in Mexico the *tucero*, whose official job is to hunt pocket gophers, is a respected member of the village society.

Strong foreclaws (left) dig burrow, marked by fan-shaped mounds of earth at entrance (above).

Slim matriarchs

To allow manoeuvrability in tunnels a tapering body is essential, and burrowing animals generally have narrow hips. On the other hand, broad hips are an asset in giving birth. In virgin pocket gophers the pelvis is very narrow, with fused pelvic bones as in other mammals, leaving too small a gap for the passage of offspring during birth. Examination after birth shows, however, an enlarged opening which just allows an easy birth. Much of the bone of the pelvic region had been dissolved away through the action of hormones secreted during pregnancy. Thus female pocket gophers have easy births, yet retain trim figures.

class	**Mammalia**
order	**Rodentia**
family	**Geomyidae**
genera	***Pappogeomys, Cratogeomys Orthogeomys, Heterogeomys Macrogeomys, Zygogeomys***

Pocket mouse

The pocket mice and spiny pocket mice, although related to the kangaroo rats (p 1215), run around on all four legs, instead of hopping on their hindlegs like kangaroo rats. They are similar in appearance, having short ears and long tails with a small tuft of hair at the tip, but both pairs of legs are the same length.

There are 25 species of pocket mice, ranging from southwest Canada to central Mexico. The head and body length varies from 2 to 5 in. and the tail is about the same length again or longer — up to 6 in. The fur is pale yellow or grey above and white underneath, with a black tip to the tail.

Eleven species of spiny pocket mice live in the deserts of central America, from the southern borders of Texas to Panama. They are a little larger than pocket mice and the fur ranges from pale grey to glossy black. Most of the hairs making up the fur are stiff and bristly. A spoonlike claw on the hindfoot is thought to be either for grooming the fur or for digging. The 10 species of forest spiny pocket mice also have bristly fur but the hairs are not so stiff. Forest spiny pocket mice are the largest, with a head and body length of 5 — 6 in. and tail up to 8 in. They live in forests from Mexico to Panama.

Underground refuges

Pocket mice spend the day enclosed in their burrows, safe from enemies and insulated from the hot, dry air.

Except for the forest spiny pocket mice, all pocket mice live in dry country where there is scanty vegetation such as sagebrush, coarse grass and short-lived flowers. Their burrows, under logs or bushes, have several entrances, usually hidden under bushes or blocked with earth. Although they stay inside during the heat of the day, pocket mice also keep out of cold or wet weather and may become dormant during cold spells. The spiny pocket mice also close their burrows when they leave them.

Sifting sand for seeds

Pocket mice feed on seeds, stripping them from plants or picking them up from the ground. They sift the sand through the long claws on their forefeet, separate the seeds and pack them into their cheek pouches. They store surplus food in side chambers of the burrow for use during times of shortage. They also eat green leaves and a few insects during wet periods when these are available. The forest spiny pocket mice, living in forests where food is more plentiful, eat more leaves and twigs as well as seeds. Pocket mice are occasionally pests when they carry off grain from fields and granaries. They do not drink; and their bodies are adapted to conserve as much water as possible so that they obtain enough from the breakdown of their dry food to supply their needs.

Soft-furred infants

The spiny pocket mice and forest spiny pocket mice breed all the year round, producing most young during spring and early summer, but pocket mice stop breeding during the height of the summer. A nest is made in the burrow and the babies are born after 3—4 weeks gestation. Litters usually number 4 babies, sometimes as many as 8, and there are 2 litters a year. The babies are born furred and even those of the spiny pocket mice have soft fur. The stiff bristles appear after the first moult at 2 months.

Pocket mice have lived over 7 years in captivity but in the wild their life expect-

△ *Desert pocket mice **Perognathus penicillatus** have long hindlegs which help support them while they dig with their forefeet. These sift sand for seeds which are placed in the external fur-lined cheek pouches. They do not drink, getting water from plants.*

ancy is very short. As with all small rodents they are food for many predators, from coyotes to badgers and rattlesnakes to owls.

Handy carrier bags

Pocket mice get their name from the cheek pouches that they, the related kangaroo rats, and pocket gophers possess. The pouches are not merely loose cheeks which bulge out as the owner crams its mouth with food, as in hamsters. They are external pockets of skin which open to the outside beside the mouth, and are fur-lined. Those of the spiny pocket mice extend as far back as the shoulders and are filled with seeds, leaves and grass by movements of the hands which are so rapid that the human eye cannot follow them. Nesting materials, too, are carried in the pouches.

A drawback to having a pouch or pocket is that it is likely to collect dirt, especially if it is used for the transport of food and bedding, so there is a risk of infection. A kangaroo's pouch is so located that it can be cleaned by licking. This is obviously impossible for a pocket mouse, but its pockets can be turned inside out for cleaning, then pulled back into place by special muscles.

class	**Mammalia**
order	**Rodentia**
family	**Heteromyidae**
genera	***Heteromys*** *forest spiny pocket mice* ***Liomys*** *spiny pocket mice* ***Perognathus*** *pocket mice*

Pogonophore

The name of these marine animals means literally 'beard-bearers', and if the name sounds mildly ridiculous, this is in keeping with the whole history of the group. The pogonophores represent a branch of the animal kingdom that was completely unknown until 1914, and which attracted little attention even among marine zoologists until little more than 10 years ago. Yet they seem now to be the most widespread and abundant sea animals.

The 100 or more known species of pogonophores are worm-like and extremely slender; a 5in. individual being $\frac{1}{80}$ in. thick. Most are a few inches long; the largest is just over a foot. Each lives in a transparent horny tube little wider than itself, but five times as long, which has ring-like markings at intervals along its length. The animal itself is made of different sections, each having a slightly different shape. In front is a long tentacle or tentacles—there may be as many as 200 or more in some species—fringed with pinnules. At the rear end are spines, or short bristles, like those on the bodies of earthworms and marine bristleworms. They probably help the animal to move up and down inside its tube. No mouth or other special organs have yet been identified.

These animals have now been found in all oceans, mainly at great depths, down to 25 000 ft, but in recent years some have been discovered in shallower water, at depths of 70 ft.

Mystery tube-dwellers

Dredged up and kept alive for only a few hours, living pogonophores are difficult to observe. Their way of life has to be deduced from what can be seen in the dead animal. They live only where the seabed is fine mud, and seem to spend most of their time inside semi-permeable tubes, through which water can pass. This may be important to the animal inside the tube because incoming water would bring oxygen for breathing. Studies at very high magnification with electron microscopes have shown a complicated body structure, including a nerve network and blood vessels containing red blood with haemoglobin. No digestive organs have been seen. The nearest thing they have to a brain is a group of nerve cells, the ganglionic mass. Tests made with living pogonophores showed that they reacted only slightly to being touched.

A question of feeding

There has been much speculation about the way pogonophores feed, as to whether they take particles of food from the water by gripping them with the pinnules on the tentacles or whether the pinnules give out a sticky secretion to which the particles adhere. Another suggestion has been that the tentacles may sweep the surface of the mud for particles. Where there are many tentacles they form tubes or complicated spirals, and it is believed food may be caught and digested in these, as in a sort of external stomach. These tentacles may also secrete fluids which digest the food externally, the food then being absorbed through the skin. The most favoured view is that these animals absorb nutrients dissolved in the seawater through their skin, but all these suggestions are no more than inspired guesses.

▽ *A rare photograph of the recently discovered species* **Oligobrachia ivanovi** *from the north east Atlantic. This large pogonophore is seen partly removed from its tube, its seven tentacles coiled up into an orange mass (× 10).*

Pieces of the breeding jigsaw

Some pogonophores that have been examined have contained large yolky eggs, others have had sperms enclosed in capsules, or spermatophores. There is nothing to show whether the sperms are merely liberated into the sea to find their way to ova in other individuals, or whether pogonophores join together in some simple form of mating. Estimates have been made of how densely they live. These vary from 50 to 500 per sq yd, but even the more densely crowded would have difficulty in contacting each other. The most reasonable assumption seems to be that the sperms are liberated into the sea, yet the fact that they are in a capsule, would suggest that the male places them on the female, or in her tube. Embryos and larvae have been found in some of the tubes. The embryos are rounded, with two girdles of cilia around the front and the rear ends. As the cilia beat in a wave-like action the embryo slowly revolves on its axis. Later, the embryo grows longer, into what may be called a larva, in which the future hair-like adult pogonophore is foreshadowed.

The youngest phylum

The very existence of the phylum Pogonophore was entirely unknown and wholly unsuspected until 1914, when specimens were examined by the French zoologist Professor M Caullery. These had been collected by the Dutch research ship *Siboga* dredging in the seas of the Malay Archipelago. He worked on them from 1914 to 1944 but was unable to find any relationship between them and other animals. He named them *Siboglinum* after the Dutch ship, *linum* being Latin for flax or linen thread. Then, in 1933, more were dredged up in the Pacific, and the view began to be taken that they were degenerate bristleworms. Soviet research ships began to find large numbers of pogonophores in the Sea of Okhotsk and later in the Indian Ocean, Antarctic and Atlantic Oceans. The Russian zoologist AV Ivanov decided, in 1955, that they represented a new phylum, which he named the Pogonophora. In plain terms an entirely new section of the animal world had been discovered.

The pogonophores have been described as looking like threads, like bits of string, or like trawl twine—or even contemptuously as looking like chewed string! We know now that research ships at sea had been finding masses of these tangled threads in their dredges. They cluttered the decks when the dredges were emptied onto them and on a British research ship they were given the name of the Gubbinidae—and shovelled back into the sea ('gubbins' is a slang name, often used by scientists, for unidentifiable 'insignificant' rubbish!). This alone shows how abundant they are on the ocean bed. It also shows why nobody took any notice of them; they looked like fibrous rubbish.

There is a great deal yet to be learned about the pogonophores. Some of it may shed light on the evolutionary history of the vertebrates. The current opinion is that they are most closely related to the supposed forerunners of the vertebrates, such as the acorn worm (p 9).

phylum	**Pogonophora**
order	**Athecanephria**
order	**Thecanephria**

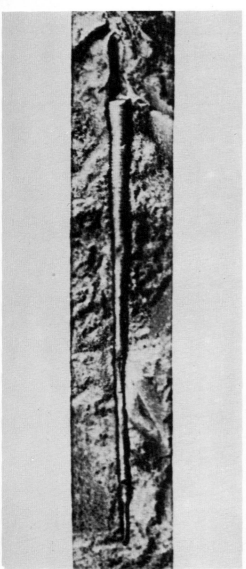

Ancestral pogonophore—the tapering tube of the fossil **Hyolithellus**, *buried over 500 million years ago in Cambrian rocks in Greenland. The indentation above the tube probably marks the position of the animal when feeding (× 8).*

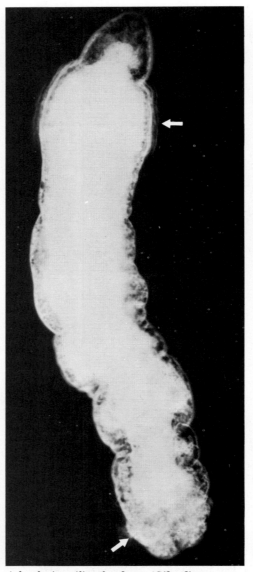

A developing ciliated embryo of **Siboglinum** *removed from its mother's tube. There is a broad ciliated band on the protosoma below the apical cone, and another smaller band at the end of the body on the metasoma (arrowed) (× 160).*

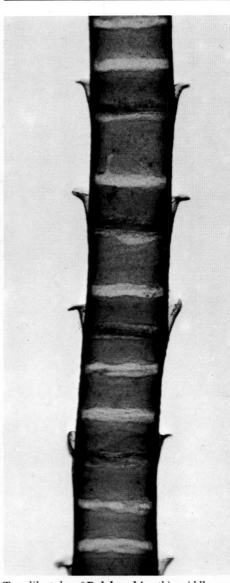

Tree-like tube of **Polybrachia**, *this middle section has membranous frills. Like many small pogonophores it has ring markings and is divided into segments. The rigid tube is composed of chitin and proteins (× 5).*

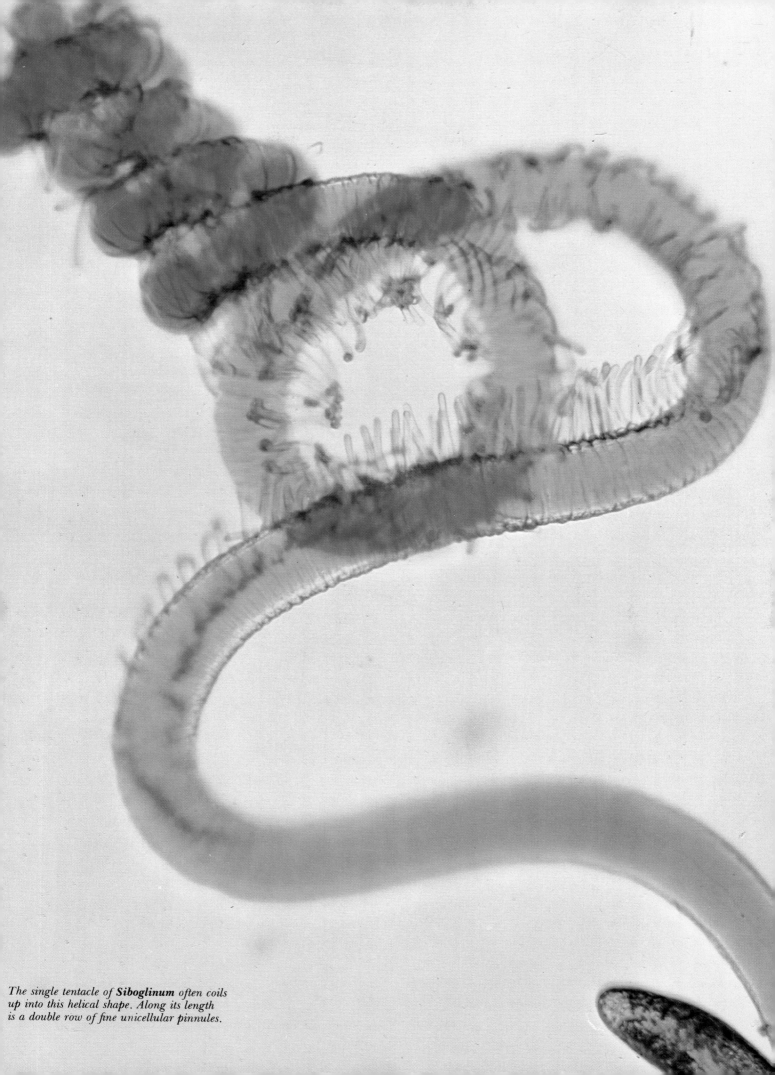

The single tentacle of **Siboglinum** often coils
up into this helical shape. Along its length
is a double row of fine unicellular pinnules.

Polar bear

The polar bear is one of the largest and the most carnivorous of all bears. The males average 7–8 ft long and may reach 9 ft, with a height of 5 ft at the shoulder. The average weight is 900 lb and the maximum over half a ton. The females are smaller, with an average weight of 700 lb. Polar bears have a long head with small ears, and a 'Roman' nose, a long neck, powerful limbs, broad feet with hairy soles, and a mere stump of a tail. Their coat, white with a yellowish tinge, is made up of long guard hairs and a dense underfur.

Their home is along the southern edge of the Arctic pack ice. Although they can swim strongly, they avoid stretches of open water and fast ice. They are carried southwards by the ice in spring and summer and return northwards when the ice breaks up.

Polar bear *(Thalarctos maritimus)*

occasional visitor

◁ *Overleaf: Queen of the castle. A polar bear isolated with her cubs keeps an eye open for intruders on the pack ice of the Arctic. The cubs remain with the mother until they are about two years old, and sometimes are allowed to cling to her as she swims along.*

▷ *A solitary polar bear steps carefully over the rocks of the Arctic. Polar bears are nomadic and roam for miles in search of food.*
▽ *A happy family — two cuddly cubs satisfy their hunger. Polar bear cubs stay with their mother until she is ready to mate again.*

A home of ice and water

Polar bears are expert divers and swim strongly, at about 6 mph, using only the front legs, and trailing the hindlegs. A thick layer of fat under the skin, 3 in. thick on the haunches, helps to keep them buoyant. Polar bears have been seen swimming strongly 200 miles from land. They usually swim with the head stretched forward, but when the sea is rough they put their heads underwater, lifting them periodically to breathe. The fat layer keeps out the cold. When it comes onto land the polar bear shakes itself like a dog.

Polar bears can walk easily over ice because of their hairy soles, and when pursued can run at speeds of up to 18 mph. They swing their heads from side to side as they walk, as if searching or smelling out prey. Essentially nomadic, they wander for miles in search of food.

Preying on seals

Their favourite food is seals, especially the ringed seal, which the bears stalk by taking advantage of snow hummocks. A seal asleep on the edge of the ice falls easy prey. The polar bear swims underwater to the spot, comes up beneath the seal and crushes its skull with one blow of the powerful forepaw. When a ringed seal is about to pup she digs an igloo in a hummock of snow over her breathing hole. Polar bears sniff out the igloos and take the pups. They are said also to hold down a pup with one paw so that its struggles attract the mother within reach of the bear. They will kill young walruses, but in a fight with a grown walrus the bear is likely to come off second best. The bears also eat fish, seabirds — at times their eggs, too — and carrion. A stranded whale will draw bears from a large area. Such a carcase once attracted 24 bears. At certain times of the year, usually in late spring or early summer, polar bears will eat large quantities of grass, lichens, seaweed, moss and other plants, and they are fond of crowberries, bilberries and cranberries.

Cubs driven away

Mating is in April or May and after a gestation of 240 days usually 2 cubs are born in December and January. At birth each cub is a foot long and weighs 1½ lb. It has a coat of short sparse hair. The eyes open at 33 days, the ears at 26 days, although hearing is imperfect until the cub is 69 days old. It starts to walk at about 47 days and is not weaned for 3 months. The cubs stay with the mother until they are at least 10 months old, often longer. When she is ready to mate again, she drives away any remaining cubs, which are by then 200–400 lb weight. Polar bears are sexually mature at 2½–5 years, the females maturing later than the males. Most of this detailed information, which would be difficult to collect in the wild, has come from records of successful breedings in zoos where some polar bears have lived well. Since polar bears are now being rapidly exterminated to satisfy the taste of the affluent for luxurious rugs it is as well that zoos have mastered the art of breeding these fierce but beautiful beasts.

No hibernation

It is often said that cubs are born while the mother is hibernating. Polar bears, like

Jurg Klages

other bears, do not hibernate in the strict sense and it is now usual to speak of their sleep as winter dormancy. The pregnant she-bear seeks out a bank of snow in the lee of a hill and digs into it. There is difference of opinion as to whether the males 'hibernate'. It seems likely that some do, but for shorter periods than the females.

Man the enemy

Apart from man the polar bear has no enemies, if we except the walrus that may gore it in self-defence. Young bears die of accidents, by being drowned or crushed by ice during storms. Old males will kill and eat the cubs, given the opportunity. Polar bears have long been hunted by the Eskimos for their meat and their pelts. Their long canine teeth, too, are used for ornaments. Bed covers, sledge robes and trousers are made from the pelt. Although Eskimos eat the flesh the liver is not used, not even to feed the dogs. Its poisonous quality is said

to be due to the high concentrations of vitamin A, which causes headaches and nausea, and sometimes a form of dermatitis.

Conserving the bear

CR Harrington, writing in *Canadian Audubon,* tells us that the earliest known record of polar bears taken into captivity was for 880 AD, when two cubs were taken from Iceland to Norway. 'At that time the animals were commonly offered to European rulers, who rewarded the donors on various occasions with ships carrying cargoes of timber or even bishoprics.' Intensive hunting of the bear began in the 17th century when whalers reached the pack ice. Two centuries later polar bears were decreasing in many parts of the Arctic. Then came the turn of the sealers, and in 1942 alone Norwegian sealers killed 714. More recently the Eskimos have been hunting the bears not for their own use but to trade the pelts. In parts of arctic

North America it is easy to land by aeroplane and shoot the bears for sport, but legislation controlling this is under fairly constant review. In 1965 Harrington estimated the world population at over 10 000 with a total annual kill of about 1 300. In September of that year an international conference decided that each nation taking part should make a study of polar bears in its territory. The results of these studies have not yet been published but will include information on the life-history, ecology, seasonal movements and population changes.

class	**Mammalia**
order	**Carnivora**
family	**Ursidae**
genus & species	***Thalarctos maritimus***

Taking the plunge. Protected by its thick layer of fat, a polar bear braves the cold waters of the Arctic where it may swim for miles out to sea.

Fred Bruemmer

Portrait of a polecat in its typical stance, long, slightly cylindrical body slung low, long neck stretched out and an inquisitive expression.

Polecat

The unpleasant discharge from its glands gave the polecat, or fitchew, its former English name of foumart or foul-marten. Because of this its fur, sold under the name 'fitch', is considered by some to be useless, but it was widely used in the early 19th century and is still used to a slight extent today.

The male polecat is about 20 in. long, of which about 5½ in. is bushy tail, and weighs up to 3 lb. The female is slightly smaller and only a little over half the weight. In both sexes the long coarse fur is dark brown on the upper parts with dense yellowish underfur showing through, and black on the underparts. The short legs and tail are black, as is the head, which has white or yellow patches between the small ears and eyes from June to November. These tend to join over the eyes in winter and, rarely, to join up with a chin patch. In a limited area of Cardiganshire, in Wales, a 'red' variety of polecat sometimes occurs, in which the coat is red, ginger or fox-coloured.

The polecat is still common throughout Europe as far north as southern Sweden and southern Finland. In the British Isles, however, it has become very rare except in Wales. Indeed, in mid-Wales, its numbers seem to be increasing.

Snake-in-the-grass

The polecat's long, almost cylindrical body moves at speed as it slinks across bare ground or close-cropped grass, with its body slung so low that it seems to be touching the ground. The long neck is stretched out and the short legs move almost in a paddling action, so the animal seems to glide rather than run. Seen from the side, the action of the limbs is more reminiscent of swimming than of running.

Taken young, polecats are easily tamed, and give little sign of their traditional smell, probably because this is used in the wild to mark a territory, not, as was formerly thought, as a defence. They also deposit urine and faeces along their trails to mark them. They spend a lot of time playing together; they will tumble over each other in a bunch, endlessly wrestling or romping—a mass of supple bodies. A significant part of this is that they grip each other by the back of the neck. This, it seems, is how they develop the neck bite used to kill their prey.

Versatile predator

A remarkable feature of the polecat is the great variety of habitats in which it can flourish. It is found in Wales from the coast right up into the hills, and is as much at home among sand dunes and on sea cliffs as it is about lowland farms or wooded gorges. It prefers, however, woods and copses, making its den in any suitable hole, such as a fox earth, rabbit burrow or natural rock crevice. A wood-stack has sometimes been used. With the approach of winter, polecats may seek shelter in deserted buildings. They are less agile than martens, and cannot climb as well as they do. They are active mainly at night, depending on a keen sense of smell to hunt down prey. They are usually silent but occasionally use short yelps, clucks and chatterings. They also scream and hiss when frightened, as part of a 'defensive threat'.

Kittens in the larder

The polecat feeds on rats, mice and rabbits, birds and their eggs, frogs, lizards and snakes. It is said to kill vipers and to be immune to their poison. The bodies of three kittens, known to have been drowned at least a quarter of a mile away, were once found in the larder of a polecat bitch. The usual method of carrying smaller prey is to grip it by the middle of the back, much as a retriever carries game.

It is usual, when speaking of polecats or any other small carnivore, to stress that they are adept at getting into hen-houses and that they have been known to kill all the occupants instead of just taking one. Indeed, the name is said to be from the French *poule chat*, the chicken cat. Accusations of poultry-killing may be justified to some extent. JG Wood, writing in 1852, said that the polecat was common in every part of England, but he also described it as 'dreadfully destructive to the poultry'. He tells of somebody's dog digging a polecat from its burrow and bringing out a whole brood of ducklings, previously lost by a farmer. Predators like the polecat, however, may help keep the populations of small mammals, especially rats and mice, within bounds. The wholesale reduction in the numbers of polecats might have contributed in the past to the calamitous increase in the populations of rats.

One litter only?

The polecat mates in early spring, probably in April, and the gestation period is about 6 weeks. Litters of 3–8, usually 5–6, are born in a nest of dry grass in woods or among rocks. The babies are blind for their first fortnight and are pure white, the colours and markings of the adults, appearing at about 3 months. It has been said that there is probably a second litter a few months later. This is unlikely since the young do not leave their parents until 3 months old, which would push the time of a second litter to late summer or early autumn. Baby polecats huddle in the nest to keep warm, but in hot weather lie as far from each other as possible. A female polecat in captivity was seen to wet her belly in her water-dish then curl herself around the babies to cool them. Another seemed to be teaching her babies to hunt. She would carry meat into the nest then drag it out, leaving a scent trail for them to follow to reach it. Whether this happens in the wild is not known.

Rapid extermination

According to L Harrison Matthews in *British Mammals*, the polecat was 'formerly a very common animal even close to London up to about a hundred years ago, whose rapid extermination over most of the country began with the first use of gin traps'. At the beginning of the 19th century it was still widely distributed throughout

Polecat (*Mustela putorius*)

England, Wales and Scotland, and records show that a total of 400 polecat pelts were sold at the old Fur Fair at Dumfries, in Scotland in 1829, and 600 in 1831. In 1866, however, the number of furs for sale at the fair was only six, after which they ceased to be included in the records. In parts of the Highlands the polecat survived longer and in Argyllshire was not uncommon about 1880. In the counties of Inverness, Ross and Sutherland it even survived into the present century but soon after 1907 the Scottish polecats seem to have become extinct and there has been no authentic record there in the past 50 years.

In England the polecat seems to have survived for as long or longer than in Scotland. Early this century it still lingered from Surrey westward to Cornwall, in woods in Lincolnshire, in several of the central counties, and in Cumberland.

Many years ago polecat-hunting was practised among the country squires of North Wales, Cheshire, Cumberland and Westmorland, where packs of hounds were kept specially for this.

class	**Mammalia**
order	**Carnivora**
family	**Mustelidae**
genus & species	*Mustela eversmanni* Asiatic polecat **M. putorius** *Vormela peregusna* marbled polecat

▽ *Pigeon pie? Three young polecats tuck into a pigeon, savagely tearing it apart. They also enjoy duck and poultry, to the dismay of many a farmer, although they are good ratters.*

Pollack

The pollack is probably the most handsomely coloured member of the cod family. It can be recognized especially by the jutting lower jaw and the lack of a barbel on the chin. Otherwise its shape conforms to the typical cod pattern, with three dorsal and two anal fins, small pectoral fins, and very small pelvic fins lying under the throat. It is dark green on the back, shading to light green on the sides, which are streaked and spotted with yellow. The belly is white. The fins are dark yellowish green and the eye golden. The lateral line is dark and strongly curved over the pectoral fin. Pollack are up to 2 ft long, exceptionally 2½ ft, and the line-caught record is 23½ lb. They range from Norway to the Mediterranean.

The origins of the name are unknown, and it has been variously altered in the past to pollock, podlok and podley. The first of these names was taken to North America and given to the coalfish, (p 458) the pollack's nearest relative.

Midwater feeders

Pollack are more a coastal fish than any other member of the cod family. They are often taken by line fisherman from the shore and when hooked they dive powerfully for refuge among the rocks. The pollack is not highly esteemed for its flesh, although it is regarded as a good sport fish. It is plentiful especially off Scotland where it is known as the lythe. Pollack come to the surface at night and are readily attracted by lights.

Mackerel fishers often catch them with bright, moving baits. Their preference for moving bait gives a clue to their food. They feed in midwater on small fish, especially sand eels, sprats, herring and pilchard. They rarely stoop to feed on the bottom, on worms, crustaceans and molluscs.

Junior marathons

Pollack spawn from February to May. The small, widely separated spawning grounds are in depths of 300 ft or less. Because the spawning grounds are so scattered – as far apart as the western English Channel and the Hebrides – young pollack make long migrations as they spread out around the coasts. The eggs, $\frac{1}{20}$ in. diameter, float near the surface. The young fish feed on the seabed, on crustaceans, worms and molluscs.

Delusory armour

Many people regard scales as a protection, so it is worth noting a remark by Dr Douglas Wilson in his *Life of the Shore and Shallow Seas*. He points out that when catching pollack for the aquarium it is better to use hooks than a net and not to hold the fish in the hand when removing the hook: 'a torn jaw nearly always heals but a few lost scales generally end in death'. Shore fishes, more liable to be thrown about by waves, do not easily bruise. They usually have no scales or only tiny ones embedded in, or else firmly fixed to, the skin.

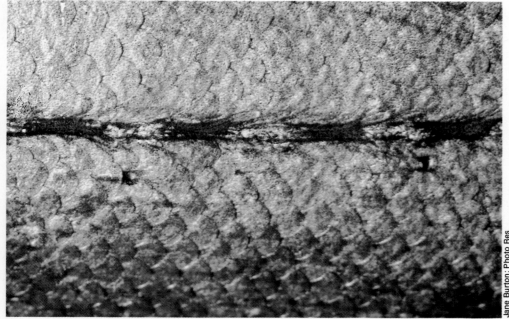

Jane Burton: Photo Res

class	**Pisces**
order	**Gadiformes**
family	**Gadidae**
genus & species	***Pollachius (Gadus) pollachius***

◁ *The lateral line and tiny scales of pollack.*
▽ *Pollack, the most handsome member of the cod family swimming with bib* **Trisopterus luscus.**

Kendall McDonald

Pompadour fish

This fish from the rivers of the Amazon basin has been described as the noblest among aquarium fishes. Its name of pompadour is then quite appropriate although it is also known as the discus from its shape. The pompadour fish and its relative, which is divided into subspecies known as the green discus, brown discus and blue discus, are almost disc-shaped when fully grown and up to 8 in. long. The long dorsal and anal fins make the otherwise oval body look more nearly circular. The body is covered with small scales but the cheeks and gill covers are more markedly scaly. The mouth is small, with thick lips. There is a single row of small conical teeth in the middle of each jaw and instead of the usual two pairs, there is a single pair of nostrils.

The colours are not easy to describe because they change with age. A young pompadour fish is brown with several vertical dark bars down each side. At 6 months old, flecks of blue appear on the head and gill covers, and these spread until the sides are coloured with alternating bands of blue and reddish brown and there are nine vertical dark bands, the first running through the eye. The fins become blue at their bases, pale blue and orange on the outer edges, and there are streaks of blue and orange between. The pelvic fins are red with orange tips. The green discus is mainly green with 9 dark vertical bars, the brown discus mainly brown with 9 dark bars and the blue discus brown with 9 blue bars.

△ Turning blue with age, pompadour fish **Symphysodon aequifasciata**. At 6 months the head and gill covers become flecked with blue and this gradually spreads across the sides.

Hanging by a thread

Pompadour fishes usually spend the day sheltering in the shadows of water plants when they are not feeding and they avoid strong sunlight. They eat water insects, especially the larvae of midges and small dragonflies, small worms and similar invertebrates. There is a brief courtship, during which the pair clean the surface of a broad leaf of a water plant. When this is ready, the female lays rows of eggs on it. Sometimes the surface of a stone is used but only after being meticulously cleaned. Once the eggs are laid the male swims over and fertilises them. The parents take it in turn to fan them with their fins and they hatch in about 50 hours. As each baby breaks out of the egg it is removed in the parents' mouth and placed on a leaf, where each hangs by a short thread for the next 60 hours. The parents continue to fan with their fins and when, at the end of this time, the babies are about to swim, they swarm on the side of one of the parents and appear to hang there. After a time the parent gives a wriggle and the fry are shaken off towards the side of the other parent, who is swimming nearby. When 3—4 weeks old the fry become independent and feed on small animal plankton such as very small water fleas or their larvae. At first they are the normal fish shape, if a little plump in the body. The discoid shape comes with age.

Baby food in doubt

There can be little doubt that baby pompadours get protection by swarming on the side of the parent, although sometimes they are eaten by the parents, at least in aquaria. The question is whether they get something more. In 1959 Dr WH Hildeman reported observations that seemed to show that the babies fed on a slime secreted by the parents' skin. This seems to have been accepted by students of tropical fishes. In the 1969 edition of their book *All about tropical fish* Derek McInerny and Geoffry Gerard not only state that the parents secrete a whitish mucus over their bodies but that the fry will eat nothing else. They quote Mr R Skipper 'who has successfully raised several spawnings' and he claims they will not thrive on any alternative food. Indeed, he maintains the only hope of raising them is to leave them with their parents. Against this we have the words of Gunther Sterba, in his *Freshwater fishes of the world*, that not only do the young of some other cichlid fishes cling to the sides of their parents but that at least one aquarist has reared young pompadours away from their parents.

One reason why pompadours are not more often kept in aquaria is that young ones taken in the wild are infected with micro-organisms. The frequent changes of water necessary to keep them in captivity seem to favour the parasites, which get the upper hand and kill the pompadours.

class	**Pisces**
order	**Perciformes**
family	**Cichlidae**
genus & species	*Symphysodon aequifasciata* brown, green and blue discus *S. discus* pompadour fish

▽ *Floating discs of colour,* **Symphysodon discus** *swim in the shadows.*

John Tashjian

Shadow and symmetry—even the pond skater's leg hairs make a beautiful pattern on the water. Overleaf: A perfectly balanced pond skater spreads its legs out on the glassy surface of the water.

Grappling iron? Pond skater's leg with water resistant hairs and a claw for catching prey.

Pond skater

Pond skaters, or water striders, are the familiar insects that can be seen floating or skimming swiftly over the surfaces of ponds, streams and flooded ditches. Their bodies are flat, narrow, and $\frac{1}{4} - \frac{3}{4}$ in. long. They appear to have only two pairs of legs, but the front pair are short and held close to the head, just behind the antennae. The rear two pairs are long and the tips are fringed with hairs, which rest on the surface of the water. Some species are wingless, others have small wings while a few have fully developed wings. Pond skaters develop through a series of moults from a small nymph. An adult bug can usually be distinguished from a nymph by its fully developed wings, but adult pond skaters are not so easily recognised because one with small wings could be a nymph or an adult, depending on the species.

While true pond skaters belong to the family Gerridae, other bugs that float on the surface of water are sometimes called pond skaters. These include the water measurer, or water gnat, family Hydrometridae, which has a curious long, narrow head and the water crickets of the family Veliidae. There are also the pondweed bugs of the family Mesoveliidae. One member is terrestrial, living among fallen leaves in the forests of New Guinea.

Running on water

Pond skaters often gather in groups along the edges of ponds and lakes, scuttling over the water when disturbed and then regrouping. They are propelled by the long pair of middle legs and steered by the hindlegs. When moving slowly, each flick of the legs sends the pond skater sliding several inches over the surface of the water, but they also hop across the water, rising an inch or so at each bound. Water plants present no obstacle and pond skaters walk over floating weed and even over dry water lily leaves.

Pond skaters prey on dead or dying insects which fall onto the water, grasping with their front legs and piercing the bodies of the prey with their mouthparts and sucking them dry. Cannibalism is common. Prey is detected by sight or by vibrations picked up by sense organs on the legs. One European species lives in estuaries and is also found around the coasts of the Baltic Sea. Pond skaters of the genus *Halobates* are among the very few marine insects. They live in tropical and subtropical seas, sometimes hundreds of miles from land, skimming over the waves and feeding on floating dead animals.

Adult hibernation

In temperate regions there are one or two generations of pond skaters each year, depending on the species. The second generation hibernates on land, but occasionally takes to water on warm winter days. In the spring and early summer they return to water and mate. About 100 eggs are laid in groups on submerged or floating plants and covered with mucilage. They hatch in about 2 weeks, depending on the water temperature, and a month later the nymphs finally change into adults.

Invisible support

The best time to watch pond skaters is on a sunny day. The tip of each leg can be seen to be in a dent in the water surface. If the water is shallow the shadows of the pond skaters can be seen on the bottom, and each leg is surrounded by a round shadow made by this dip. It is caused by the weight of the pond skater pressing the legs into the water, but it does not sink because the force of surface tension is counteracting this weight. The surface tension is due to a film of closely linked water molecules on the surface of the water which acts like a very fine rubber sheet. It is a very weak sheet and normally we do not notice it. It is this force of surface tension that holds a drop of water in a globule on a polished surface instead of spreading out in a film. The capacity of surface tension to keep objects afloat can be demonstrated by floating a cigarette paper in a glass of water and gently placing a needle on it. Eventually the paper becomes waterlogged and sinks, but the needle remains afloat—held up by surface tension.

Pond skaters sometimes enter the water completely but can refloat themselves because the undersides of their bodies are covered with a dense pile of hairs that traps air and prevents the body from becoming wetted. It has been said that a marine *Halobates* becomes wetted and drowned if a drop of rain lands on its back, but if this is so it is surprising that they have not been wiped out by tropical storms.

phylum	**Arthropoda**
class	**Insecta**
order	**Hemiptera**
family	**Gerridae**
genus & species	*Gerris lacustris* **G. thoracicus** **G. remigis** *others*

Pond snail

To some people, any kind of freshwater snail is a pond snail, even if it lives more often in rivers. The name, however, is usually restricted to those snails with pointed spires and more or less oval mouths to their shells that make up the family Lymnaeidae. They are the commonest freshwater snails in both Europe and in North America.

Freshwater snails are of two main kinds. One group includes the river snails **Viviparus** and valve snails **Valvata** which, with their marine relatives, can close the openings of their shell with a lid, or operculum. The others lack opercula, and are called Pulmonata because they have a lung, formed by the mantle cavity. The true pond snails, those we are dealing with here, belong to the second group, as do the bladder snails **Physa** and ramshorns or trumpet snails **Planorbis** and **Planorbarius**. These are called wheel snails in North America. In the true pond snails there is a lobe of tissue by the opening of the lung that forms a breathing tube, a kind of snorkel.

One of the largest species is the great pond snail which grows to about 2 in. long, depending largely on the volume of water in which it has grown. At the other extreme, a full grown dwarf pond snail may reach only $\frac{1}{3}$ in. Unlike the shells of trumpet snails and bladder snails, those of pond snails are usually coiled to the right; the whorls increase in a clockwise direction as seen from the tip of the spire. In the ear pond snail the last whorl of the shell is greatly expanded, to give the whole an 'ear' shape, and this peculiarity is taken to an extreme in the bubble-thin shell of the glutinous snail. This species is unique in that the mantle tissue can spread outside the shell and all but cover it, so making the snail look like a little dab of glue. The shells of pond snails are generally a dark or pale horn colour and are carried with the spire directed backwards. The ear pond snail, however, points its spire to one side.

On the head are two non-retractile tentacles, each with an eye at the base, and in these respects the pond snails and other freshwater Pulmonata, known collectively as Basommatophora ('basal-eyed ones') contrast with the garden snail and other Stylommatophora ('stalk-eyed ones'). The latter have two pairs of tentacles which can be pulled into the body and the eyes are borne at the tips of the hindmost pair.

Not always in ponds

Pond snails creep along by waves of muscular contractions moving forward over the foot, and sometimes crawl upside down at the surface of the water. Some pond snails, like the great pond snail, crawl to the sur-

An adaptable species, the wandering pond snail can live in a number of habitats, and survive long periods of drought. Unlike most pond snails it eats both plant and animal matter.

face at intervals to renew the air in their lungs. If they cannot reach the surface, as when they are under ice, they accelerate their normal skin breathing. There are some species that depend entirely on the exchange of gases through the skin and have their 'lungs' permanently filled with water. Pond snails have also been known to survive being frozen in ice.

Pond snails live in a variety of freshwater habitats, though with the exception of the ubiquitous wandering snail, they do not colonise very soft or acid water. While some require large bodies of water, others, like the marsh snail and the dwarf pond snail, flourish in ditches or simply on wet mud, and can survive long periods of drought. A wandering snail has been known to survive 4 years in a dry aquarium, that had been stored away in an attic.

Cannibal snails

Some pond snails live mainly on scum-like algae and other plant material, which is why they are kept in aquaria, to keep the glass cleaned of algae. On the other hand, the great pond snail feeds on animal as well as plant matter and will even kill such lively animals as newts, sticklebacks and the larvae of water beetles. Some species will eat carrion or even resort to cannibalism. All rasp their food to tiny fragments with their file-like tongue, or radula, which is covered with thousands of teeth (see picture on page 6).

Mating chain reactions

Pond snails are hermaphrodite, each individual having male and female organs opening separately to the exterior. In the dwarf pond snail, a single individual fertilises itself. Tens of thousands have been reared in the laboratory without cross-

fertilisation being seen. Usually one individual fertilises another, one taking the part of a male in every mating and the other taking the part of the female. Sometimes the one acting at that moment as a female acts simultaneously as the male to a third individual and in this way chains of mating snails may be built up. Reciprocal exchange of sperms between two snails is also possible.

Eggs are laid in gelatinous plates or cylinders attached to a firm support, with 2–100 eggs in each mass according to species and food supply. Development is rapid; in the dwarf pond snail young snails may emerge from the egg mass in 2 or 3 weeks and mature sexually within another 3 weeks.

What is a species?

To many people all pond snails must seem utterly insignificant and beneath notice. Yet, as host to the liver flukes, the dwarf pond snail has caused the deaths of millions of sheep (see fluke p 789). It is not strictly a water snail in that it flourishes on damp mud, feeding on the algae on the surface. A connection between liver rot and damp places was known for a long time but it was the discovery of the role of the snail that opened the door to effective control of the disease. Other water snails are hosts to other kinds of flukes, including human blood flukes. Each species of fluke is to some extent limited to particular snail species. Specifying the snails that support flukes is one of the main problems facing those who study the liver fluke. In Britain and many other countries, only the dwarf pond snail does so, but other species with similar habits may take its place elsewhere. Even in relation to the dwarf pond snail, however, the situation is not clear cut. At one time the classification of pond snails was in considerable confusion, but even when a large number of species names were shown to refer to only minor variations in the individuals of one species, problems still remained. The difficulty is that there is not always a clear-cut distinction between one species and another – their origin by the gradual process of evolution prevents that. Moreover, populations of snails in different parts of the range of one species may differ in the extent to which they can carry flukes and yet the snails of these various populations may look alike to our eyes. Dr CA Wright, who is studying how to combat flukes, is trying to devise chemical tests to distinguish between populations of pond snails.

phylum	**Mollusca**
class	**Gastropoda**
order	**Pulmonata**
suborder	**Basommatophora**
family	**Lymnaeidae**
genera & species	***Lymnaea trunculata*** *dwarf pond snail* ***L. palustris*** *marsh pond snail* ***L. stagnalis*** *great pond snail* ***L. auricularia*** *ear pond snail* ***L. peregra*** *wandering pond snail* ***L. catascopium*** *N American pond snail* ***Myxas glutinosa*** *glutinous snail*

△ *Glued on tight, the egg ropes of the great pond snail on the underside of pond weed.*
▽ *Great pond snails browse the algae which grows on plants, the side of the tank and on other snails.*